A HISTORY OF
ROF CHORLEY

Taken in the same filling shop as the illustration on the front cover, on
Group Six (later eight), 'C' Lines, about the same time. In this view, eight
bombs are shown being filled/assembled whilst positioned on their ends in
wooden stillages. From the notices, it would seem that the bombs are being
fitted with exploders at this stage.

A *History of the*
Royal Ordnance Factory
Chorley

MICHAEL NEVELL,
JOHN ROBERTS
and
JACK SMITH

Carnegie Publishing, 1999

First published in 1999 by
Carnegie Publishing Ltd,
Carnegie House,
Chatsworth Road,
Lancaster LA1 4SL

in collaboration with
Royal Ordnance plc
and
University of Manchester Archaeological Unit

British Library Cataloguing-in-Publication data
A catalogue record for this book is available from the British Library

ISBN 1-85936-063-7

Typeset and originated by Carnegie Publishing Ltd
Printed and bound by Redwood Books, Trowbridge

Contents

Glossary and abbreviations

AA	Anti-aircraft
ARP	Air Raid Warden
bomb	a high explosive device dropped from the air
CE	Composition Explosive
clean side	any area within an explosives filling group where access is strictly controlled
CMS	Centre for Management Studies
Cleanways	paths, often covered, that gave access between the various clean side parts of the factory without the need to move back into the dirty side
CROF	Controller, Royal Ordnance Factories
dilly	an electric trolley used to transport munitions around the factory
dirty side	any area outside an explosives filling group
ETF	Electronic Time Fuze
FEF	Fast Event Facility
GNP	Gross National Product
Group System	The Group System, which divided the site into a series of sealed units each dealing with just one aspect of the munitions filling process, allowed the free flow of munitions around the site in as safe a manner as possible
GW	Guided Weapons, such as rockets
HE	High Explosive
HER	High Explosive Research
HESH	High Explosive Squash Head
HMOW	His Majestey's Office of Works
LAW	Light Anti-armour Weapon
magazine	a blast proof building specifically designed to store munitions of all sorts

MoD	Ministry of Defence
munitions	weapons materials used in war
PE	Procurement Executive
	PIP
	Presevation, Inspection and Packing
proof yard	area on the western side of the factory where munitions were tested or 'proved' to see that they not only performed as per specification, but also to ensure that they were safe to be handled and transported
QCD	Quality Control Department
QF	quick fire ammunition
ROF	Royal Ordnance Factory
round	ammunition of one shot
scooters (or 'sprogs')	an electric vehicle used by staff to get around the factory groups
shell	an artillery round
SSIs	Superintendent's Safety Instructions
stores	any munitions kept on the factory
TNT	a type of explosive powder

Preface

THIS BOOK is intended neither as a detailed social history of ROF Chorley, nor as an extensive archaeological record of that site. Rather it is an attempt to put on record the creation, construction and continuing story of the world's largest purpose-built munitions filling factory. Drawing on a variety of sources, from oral and written evidence to photographs and the standing remains themselves, this work is a summary of over sixty years of work and life at the factory.

The King arriving at the Royal Ordnance Factory Halt, Chorley

On 31 March 1939 the royal train arrived at ROF Halt, bringing King
George VI to officially open the factory. Here he is being met by the Lord
Lieutenant of Lancashire, Lord Derby, prior to touring the factory site.

CHAPTER ONE

Introduction:
The Woolwich of the North

Royal Ordnance Factory Chorley (ROF Chorley) covers 928 acres
and is split between the historic townships of Chorley and Leyland. The 928 acres which became the site for the building of the
filling factory at Chorley has been worked by man for over one
thousand years. The first military association with the site was
during the Roman occupation of Britain, the line of the military
road, built between the Roman sites of Wigan and Walton-le-Dale
(in Preston), almost certainly passes across the factory.

   Although the factory is referred to as ROF Chorley, for hundreds
of years the site lay mostly within the ancient township and manor
of Euxton. According to popular belief the reason that the factory
was called Chorley was because of the problems with the pronun-
ciation and spelling of the name Euxton! The name is pronounced
as 'Exton', or 'Uxton', or even 'Euston'. Consequently, it was easier
to say Chorley and the site did lie within the county borough
boundaries of Chorley, created in the 1890s.[1]

   In the 1930s the ROF site was good agricultural land used for
pasture and crops, worked by seven farms. There were also large
areas of woodland and two streams flowing across the township.
Four of the farms would become totally incorporated within the
ROF site, and three others would lose much of their farmland.
Building work on the newly purchased site of ROF Chorley began
in January 1937, and in December 1938 part of the factory was
available for limited munitions production to begin. The official
opening of the factory took place on 31 March 1939 marked by
the visit of King George VI. This was the second time that this
tiny village had played host to the ruling monarch; King Charles
I was reputed to have stayed at nearby Euxton Hall in 1650.

The facts and figures pertaining to the building of the factory are outlined later, yet the headlines carried in national and local newspapers from that year capture some of the effort and excitement of this huge construction project: 'Euxton Factory Construction Smashed World Records'; 'The King Shown Munition Works Secrets'; 'The King Shown Secrets Of Vast New Arsenal'. Of all these headlines and articles, one in the *Daily Express* from 1 April 1939 was perhaps the most expressive. This reported that, 'Standing in a bombproof workshop, deep underground, the King saw yesterday some of the mysteries of Britain's new wonder munitions factory at Chorley, Lancashire, the Woolwich of the North'.[2]

When the factory came into full production during 1941 it was deemed the largest ammunition filling factory in the world. Its effect on the local community was massive, from the houses and hostels which were built for those who worked at the factory, to the presence of the United States Army Air Force (who used one of the hostels built for the ROF Chorley workers), and above all the 35,000 people who came to work there during the war.

During the immediate post-war years the factory geared itself up to produce civilian goods and helped with the rebuilding of country's infrastructure. The 1950s saw renewed munitions production, although on a much reduced scale, with most of the vast factory with its hundreds of buildings lying mothballed from this period onwards.

The Royal Ordnance Factories were privatised by an Act of Parliament on 1 January 1985, creating Royal Ordnance plc. Royal Ordnance plc was subsequently sold by the government to British Aerospace on 1 January 1987 and the company continues to operate as a wholly owned subsidiary of British Aerospace.

Over the last 12 years, major restructuring of the company has been necessary in order to remain competitive in the world market and in order to respond to the changing defence environment. This has resulted in significant site rationalisation and closures across the UK.

Notwithstanding the extensive rationalisation at the ROF Chorley site, Chorley has remained the headquarters and registered office of Royal Ordnance plc since 1990 and it continues the core activity of manufacturing initiators (small explosive devices) in support of the company's comprehensive product range, which includes small arms and medium calibre ammunition. Its manufacturing activity is core to Royal Ordnance, being Europe's largest manufacturer of small and medium calibre ammunition. Royal Ordnance Chorley is, and always was, shaped by government policy, reflecting the changing nature of the military threats to Britain and some of the changes in British society during the twentieth century.

Plate 2.1 (ref 2.3). The first buildings on the site which was to become ROF Chorley were wooden sheds used by the men working for civil engineering contractor Sir Lindsay Parkinson of Blackpool. The picture above, taken in November 1937, shows the levelling of the site, the first job undertaken prior to marking out for roads, buildings etc.

CHAPTER TWO

Founding the Factory

Government policy and the origins of Royal Ordnance Factory Chorley

The Royal Ordnance factories have their origin in the Crown's need for a constant supply of armaments for foreign campaigns and home defence. There was, however, an ever present debate as to whether the crown and the state would be best served by independent suppliers or by its own servants. In the sixteenth and seventeenth centuries it was usual for ordnance stores to be made privately or abroad, but during the eighteenth century a state owned system of factories began to develop, and as the British Empire grew in the nineteenth century so did the Royal Ordnance factories.[1]

This pattern is reflected in the history of the three earliest Royal Ordnance factories. Waltham Abbey, the Royal Gunpowder Mills Factory, was the earliest, established in the sixteenth century. It was owned and run by one family and was not taken over by the government until 1787. The origins of the Woolwich Arsenal, which was always owned and controlled by the government, lay in the 1660s. The Royal Arms Factory at Enfield was founded as a permanent factory in 1811 in response to the needs of the Napoleonic wars, although prior to that date small arms had been made on the site by private companies on licence.[2]

World War One saw a massive expansion in the capabilities of the Royal Ordnance, with dozens of national factories established in the years 1914–18. After the First World War the balance of opinion shifted away from the state production of armaments towards production by private industry. During the 1920s successive British governments held the belief that a large state maintained armaments industry was not necessary since it would

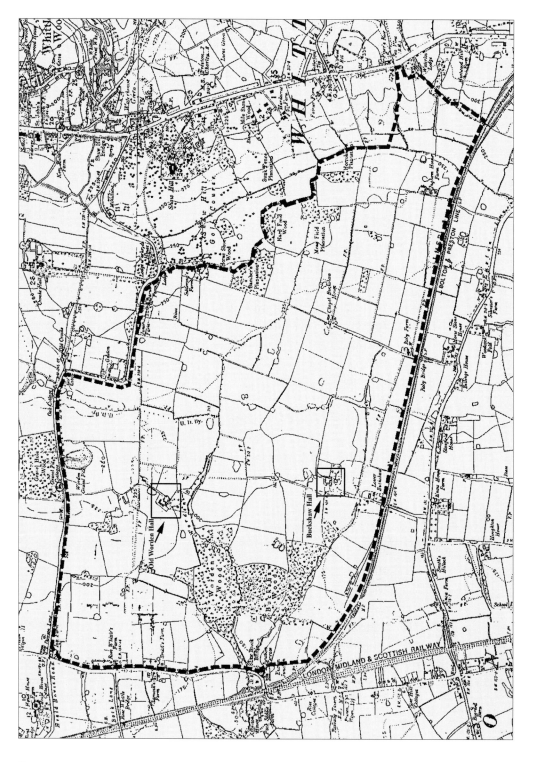

be possible to mobilise civilian industry in the event of war. This view had its origins in the 1919 report of the McKinnon Wood Committee, which had been set up to consider the fate of the Royal Ordnance Factories. Their report stated that 'during the present war a very large number of engineering firms have been educated in armament manufacture, and the basis for armament supply is now so broad that specialising in the future on the part of a limited number of firms will probably not be necessary for the safety of the country'.[3] Consequently, after the First World War the national factories were either closed or sold off and by 1922 only three Royal Ordnance Factories were left; Enfield, Waltham Abbey, and Woolwich.[4]

This policy was maintained until the early 1930s when the takeover of Germany by the National Socialist Party (Nazis) in January 1933 increased the threat of a European war and, thus, led to a decision by the British government to rearm. As early as 1931 there was disquiet in Britain and France about German rearmament,[5] but these worries did not come to a head until the collapse of the Second International Conference on Disarmament, after the withdrawal of Germany from both the Conference and the League of Nations in October 1933. A sub-committee of the Imperial Defence Committee, the Defence Requirements Committee, was formed to review British defence deficiencies and this recommended a balanced rearmament programme.[6] The pre-occupation of both the public and the British government with the threat of aerial bombardment meant that two-thirds of the money the committee had recommended for rearmament was to be spent on the Royal Air Force, to form a strategic bombing force equal to that assumed to be possessed by Germany. The prevailing strategic view in the 1930s was that there was no adequate defence against the bomber and therefore the only form of realistic defence possible was deterrence. Whilst orders for new ships for the Royal Navy suffered as a consequence of this policy it was the army that was hardest hit, with the government abandoning the idea of a British Expeditionary Force that could be committed to the European Continent.[7] This imbalance in defence priorities during the 1930s was further skewed by the world-wide economic depression of the early to mid 1930s which led to a reduction by a third in the new money envisaged by the Defence

Buckshaw Hall and Old Worden Hall and their environs in 1844. The broken line indicates the extent of the future factory to the north of the railway line.

7

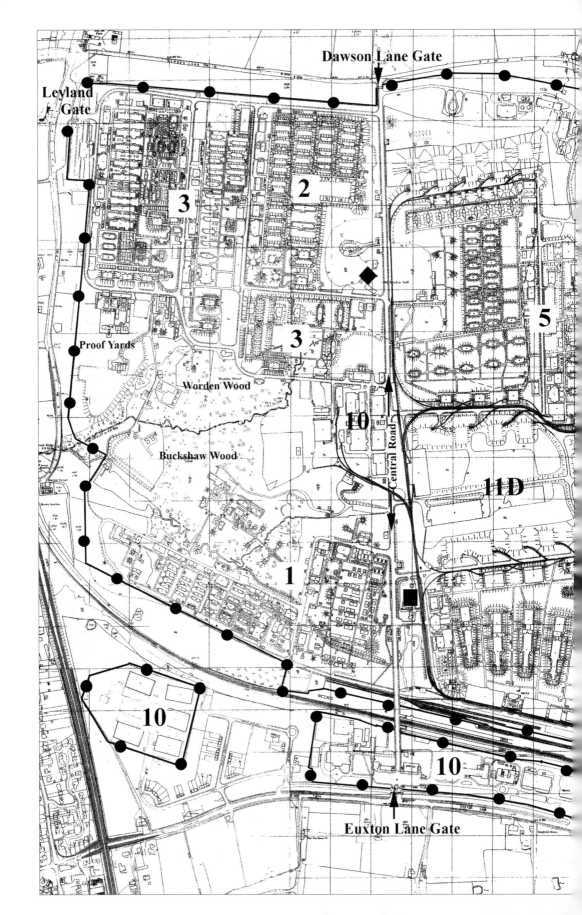

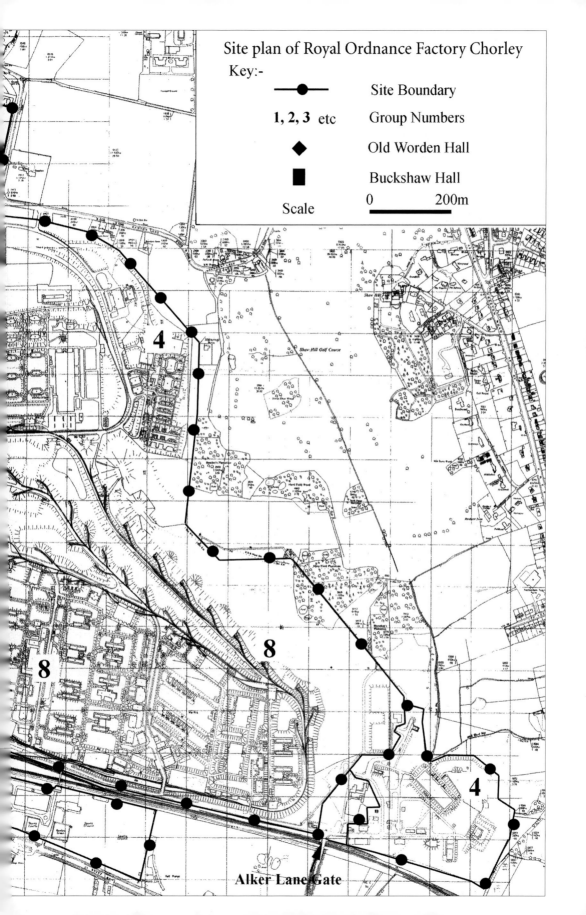

Royal Ordnance Factories, 1945.

Requirement Committee. Consequently Britain spent roughly a third of what Germany spent on rearmament during the years 1933 to 1938.

The origins of the site that was to become ROF Chorley arose from this new policy. As part of the rearmament programme a series of new supply factories were to be built in western and northern Britain away from potential enemy aerial bombardment. Three types of factory were envisaged: engineering factories which were to make guns, mountings, and shell casings; factories to manufacture explosive compositions; and filling factories which would receive the explosives and cases and then create the final product.[8] By the beginning of the Second World War in September 1939, 23 new factories had been commissioned by the government, although only seven were operational.[9]

The decision to build at Chorley

One of the earliest of the new supply factories to be commissioned, and the first and the biggest of the filling factories to be constructed, was ROF Chorley which was to incorporate the latest technology in packing chemical-based explosives and in the production of munitions. In December 1934 a committee headed by Sir Douglas Hacking recommended the removal of the Woolwich Filling Factory to a new site in the western part of the British Isles as far away from likely enemy air attack as was possible, but with access to a good communications network, proximity to other new sites, and preferably in an area with high unemployment. The site initially suggested for the new factory was at Oswestry, Shropshire.[10] However, the site conditions at Oswestry proved unsuitable, and so the search was widened to include south Wales and Lancashire. After visits to a number of potential sites in the summer of 1935 by officials from the War Office, two sites emerged as the best candidates; Bridgend in South Wales and Chorley in Lancashire. At a Cabinet meeting on 31 July 1935 it was decided to proceed with the Chorley site.

The site chosen was an area of farmland one mile to the north-west of Chorley town centre in the old township of Euxton, but within the Urban District of Chorley. It had excellent road access, a railway line at a suitable level and sandy soil. The land

11

was reasonably flat but with enough undulation to help in drainage and the traversing of buildings. There was also a ready pool of labour, with Leyland on the doorstep of the factory, the industrial town of Chorley only one mile to the east, Horwich five miles, Wigan eight miles, Preston nine miles, Blackburn ten miles, and Bolton eleven miles; a total population of approximately 450,000 in 1935. Strategically the site was not easy to distinguish from the air, whilst the nearby Pennines created meteorological difficulties for the aircraft of that period which the War Office considered a significant tactical advantage for the site.[11]

Despite local opposition from some of the farmers, in May 1936, 928 acres of farmland were purchased in Euxton at a cost of £105,000.[12] The site encompassed a number of farms within its perimeter, two of which (see *Buckshaw Hall* and *Worden Old Hall*) were ancient timber-framed buildings.[13] This was in part to maintain the full safety distance between magazines to avoid the cramped conditions typical of Woolwich Arsenal, to meet the new Public Safety Orders, and to allow room on the site for later expansion.[14] It was also the result of a number of changes in policy. In December 1934 the new site for Woolwich Arsenal was envisaged as covering 400 acres. However, between then and May 1936 the requirements for the site were significantly altered. It was decided to retain the Woolwich facility and to correlate the new production at Chorley with a second new filling factory at Bridgend. Additionally, in November 1935 a need was identified for a bulk storage facility either on site or nearby. Therefore, as early as 30 August 1935 it was recommended that if Chorley was chosen then a minimum of 900 acres should be purchased. Consequently, when the first construction contract was signed on 6 January 1937 the site of ROF Chorley had grown to cover 928 acres, with a further 43 acres at the storage facility at nearby Heapey. Yet the detailed design requirements had still to be finalised, and this drawback when combined with changes in government policy as the European political situation worsened, accounted for the more than fivefold increase in the cost of the replacement for the Woolwich Arsenal, as first envisaged by the Hacking Committee. From an original estimate of £2,100,000 in December 1934, the cost for the construction of ROF Chorley had already risen to £5,750,000 in December 1936 before building started, and the final cost was put at £11,490,700 in January 1940.[15]

Planning the factory

Once the site had been purchased a special branch of the Chief Mechanical Engineer's (CME) department was formed at Woolwich to carry out the detailed design of Chorley. Although soon afterwards the government turned over the building of all the new factories to His Majesty's Office of Works (HMOW), Woolwich remained responsible for assessing the requirements of buildings, machinery and general layout at each factory. The preliminary plans for the site were ready by November 1936, when the initial requests for tenders, with a timescale of 24 months for construction, was made. The contractor approved in December 1936 was Lindsay Parkinson of Blackpool, whose bid at £3,505,000 was £800,000 below the next contractor, with a construction timescale of 24 months.[16] The plan envisaged building the world's largest filling factory, comprising four main elements; filling facilities, storage magazines, transit sheds, and a transportation system around the site.

The general ground plan of the factory was dictated by the considerations of topography, the ease of communications around the factory, and the necessity for strict safety precautions. Thus, topography dictated that bulk magazines for the storage of High Explosive, and associated filling buildings, could only be constructed economically in the south-eastern quadrant of the site, whilst bulk magazines for cordite storage and their filling facilities were most suited to the northern area. Smaller components such as fuzes and detonators would have to be filled in the west owing to the transport difficulties on the site, whilst sections between which there was heavy traffic were to be placed together.

From the beginning, because of the varying nature of the explosive risk involved with each process, the site was to be split into small, exclusive, production sections (high explosive shell filling, cordite filling, fuze and detonator filling, and cartridge filling), although the fully developed group system did not emerge until the site was in full production (see Chapter 3). Thus, the

13

Worden Hall

Worden Old Hall, a Grade II* Listed Building, lies within the north-western quadrant of the site, on Group 2. Originally it was the home of the Farington family who bought the estate around 1549, but from the eighteenth century until it was sold in 1936 it was used as a farm. The present hall was probably built by William Farington (1537–1610), steward to the household of the Earl of Derby, and a possible model for Shakespeare's character Malvolio in the play 'Twelfth Night, or what you will'. The hall and estate were bought by the government in 1936, and in 1940 it was surveyed by Royal Ordnance, and again recently as part of a postgraduate course (Angell 1998; Farrer & Brownbill 1908). It was

used as office accommodation on and off until the 1950s. Thereafter, the hall, together with some of the farm outbuildings, was used as a Civil Defence and Fire Training centre. It is now empty.

The hall is a two-storey timber-framed building of rectangular plan. The framing comprises posts and studding, producing tall rectangular panels. It has an original roof comprising six strutted roof trusses which each have collars and trenched purlins. There are seven bays giving three rooms on each floor, whilst on the ground floor there is a cross-passage in bay five. The northern elevation has been extended in brick, probably in the eighteenth century, to give a four-gabled front façade. One gable had until 1984 a wooden plaque with the 'Sign of passion' on it, a reminder that the estate was once owned by the Knights of St John. This plaque is now in the St John museum in London.

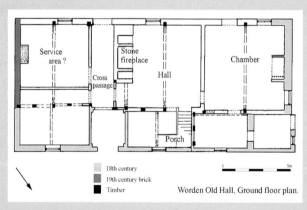

Worden Old Hall, Ground floor plan.

The earliest phase of the hall is represented by the timber-framing, which includes internally chamfered posts and trusses, and four-centred Tudor-arch style doorways with panel and baton doors, some of which have original iron strap hinges and latches. The former timber-framed northern elevation can still be seen within the building, and there is some suggestion that it may have had a timber porch. This has quatre-foil bracing to both floors and gable trusses decorated with herring bone panelling. All these features suggest a sixteenth century origin for this primary phase. The large stone and brick fireplace visible in bay 4, with its corbelled brick work supporting the hearth to the first floor, appears to be a later, probably seventeenth-century, insertion. Map evidence supported by the 1666 Hearth Tax Returns (which list 23 hearths in the building) and probate material indicate that the site was once much more extensive, with buildings to the north-west and south-east.

detonator group, where initiating compositions were manufactured and filled and where the risk was high but the quantities involved small, had buildings that were small, close together and unmounded. In contrast, the high explosive shell filling section, where the quantities were large, had all its buildings mounded and separated.[17] Inside each section the flow of work was to be from the outside towards the centre and from empty component stores to transit sheds. The accumulation of explosives in working areas was to be avoided.[18] In all, the new factory was initially to comprise 700 buildings, many of which were to be built of steel frames and brick walling, with timber shuttering. Each section was to be serviced by the factory's own internal railway network. By the time the site was completed at the end of 1939, the number of buildings on the site had risen to 1500, covering approximately 2.8 million square feet.

The project was bedevilled with construction problems from the beginning. As a result of the need for secrecy, the initial government surveys in 1935 and early 1936 were not sufficiently detailed and consequently the design of the factory had to be changed to accommodate a number of unexpected problems with the site. Firstly, as late as 22 August 1936 'no official enquiries as to the availability of water had been made', and this on a site which would need roughly two million gallons of water a day. Various options were considered, including drawing the necessary water from the Liverpool Corporation mains or tapping the Thirlmere aqueduct, but the huge quantity of water needed meant that in the short term the supply would have to come from the Lake District reservoirs, and later on from specially sunk Artesian wells.[19]

Detailed plans for the site had not been finalised when the first contract was signed in January 1937 and of necessity the design and layout of the filling process continued in tandem with building operations. To add to this problem the time scale and specifications of the project were subject to changes by the War Office, which was reacting to the deteriorating international political situation of the late 1930s. Although some flexibility to cope with new requirements was built into the factory design (for instance it was known as early as December 1936 that ROF Chorley would have to be designed to cope with filling the new 3.45″ shell then under development), when combined these two

15

Buckshaw Hall

Buckshaw Hall, a Grade II* Listed Building, lies on the eastern side of Central Road between Groups 1 and 8. Originally owned by the Anderton Family the Buckshaw estate was sold to Major Edward Robinson (d 1681) in 1652 and it was he who built the present hall in 1654 (Farrer & Brownbill 1908). A tenuous connection between the hall and arms and ammunition comes from the fact that a son of Edward Robinson, who was in the Civil War, wrote a *Discourse on the Civil War in Lancashire*. The estate was sold to John Walmsley in the nineteenth century and then passed to the Townley Parkers of Cuerdon and the Crosses of Shaw Hall. Between 1885 and 1892 it was sold to Richard Stock from whom the government purchased it in 1936. After it was purchased by the government Buckshaw Hall was used as offices, although it is now empty.

The building has two storeys and is of timber-framed construction throughout, the framing comprising uprights forming large square panels. The timber-framing is supported on a plinth of large sandstone blocks. The hall has a symmetrical façade (the western elevation) and in plan it is H-shaped, that is it has cross-wings at either end, with a baffle-entry. The two cross-wings each

comprise one bay, flanking a central smaller bay incorporating the porch with its gabled roof. Both wings have jettied first floors and gables with plaster coves and ovolo-moulded jetty bressumers carried on scrolled brackets which are integral with the wallposts. Original internal fittings include the chamfered and stopped tie-beams, and many of the panel and baton doors which still have their original iron strap hinges and latches. The dating of this phase is marked by a datestone on the northern gable, and further work in the late seventeenth century is marked by a datestone which reads 'JR 1680' in the northern cross-wing.

Subsequent alterations included the construction of the large stone back-to-back fireplaces and the rear staircase turret, both of which appear to be early to mid-eighteenth century, and a Victorian spiral staircase in the northern cross-wing. Extensive restoration of the southern wing was carried out by Colonel T. R. Crosse in 1885, and there is a datestone marking this restoration on the southern gable. Despite these alterations the hall is a fine example of seventeenth-century craftsmanship.

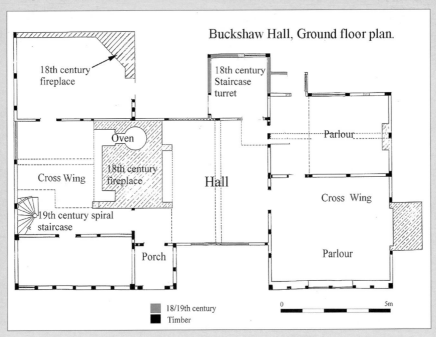

Buckshaw Hall, Ground floor plan.

18th century fireplace

18th century Staircase turret

Oven

Parlour

18th century fireplace

Cross Wing

Hall

Cross Wing

19th century spiral staircase

Parlour

Porch

Parlour

18/19th century
Timber

0   5m

factors led to escalating costs and delays in the completion of the filling factory.[20]

As part of the flexibility of the scheme the number of building types on the site was originally confined to four, the primary two being magazines for storage and a building of 60 by 30 feet with standard door and window positions which could be used for all Quick Fire (QF) work. Early in 1937 the first of the new requirements for Chorley were made. They concerned the new Anti-Aircraft (AA) programmes, and added considerably to the quantities of QF fixed ammunition and TNT poured filling that was originally planned. To put this work at Chorley, it was argued, gave 'the best factory balance and the most economical distribution of work', yet without the need to change the layout of the factory.[21] Revised requirements for the Navy soon followed. By the middle of 1937 all the spare building capacity at Chorley had been used in these adjustments, and then began the re-allocation of use of the buildings which was to cause many problems during construction. To add to these difficulties it was decided in July 1937 to add a cordite fuze powder manufacturing facility to the Chorley site.[22] When the details of the new 2lb bomb and 40mm shell programme for the army were finalised in April 1938 it was decided to shift bomb filling from Chorley to Glascoed in order to cope with the extra capacity needed. These two programmes had a complex filling procedure which included self-destroying tracers, and gunpowder and TNT pellets, which would have to be carried out away from ordinary TNT work. It also required special plant and buildings three times as large as those scheduled for the Chorley site. This meant new construction which left some of the new buildings at the factory redundant.[23] To complicate matters further the design of the 40mm shell was simplified in the autumn of 1939, which reduced the need for the new, larger, building type at Chorley. However, as these buildings were nearly completed it was decided to finish them and to reduce the projected component capacity at other new factories.[24]

Building the factory

The construction of Chorley was a new venture for the government in that it was the first and largest of the new production facilities

A wide variety of posters was used throughout the country. They covered topics such as health and safety, manufacturing procedures, attendance and production levels. Many emphasised to employees the importance of every aspect of the work done at Chorley for the war effort.

19

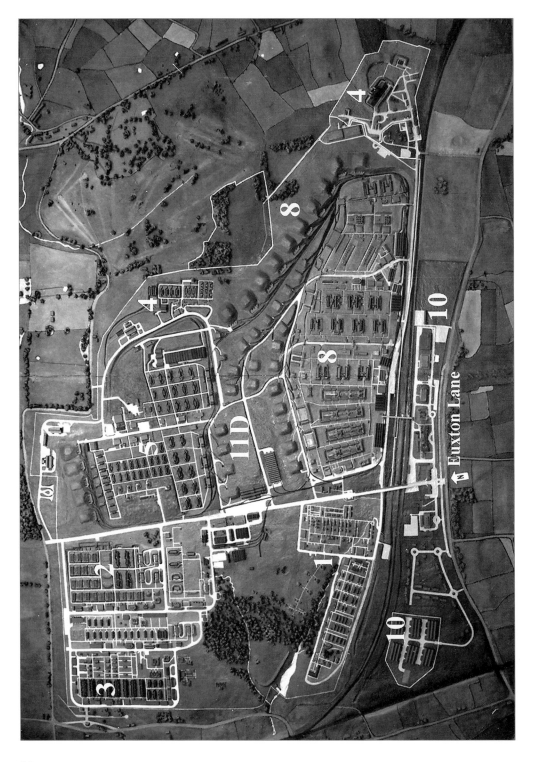

envisaged by the Hacking Committee. Consequently, construction difficulties were encountered not only because of bad weather and unexpected geological conditions (for instance the use of heavy steam powered digging equipment churned up the ground to the intended depth of the foundations for the buildings, necessitating deeper foundations) but because this was the first project of its kind. As it was difficult to suggest any order or priority for sections or buildings, it was made clear to the contractors that the factory should be completed as a whole, without the use of temporary buildings, so construction was to be primarily in brick and steel, as the cheapest available materials.[25]

During the first half of 1937 considerable extra expenditure was incurred through unexpected difficulties with the topography of the site itself; difficulties which were explained as the result of not having the time to undertake all the boreholes and test pits necessary to test the subsoil before purchase. Thus, it was found that there was a drop of 100 feet in the ground level of the site between the north-eastern and the south-western perimeters. As it was not found practicable to level the site to compensate for this drop it became impossible to arrange for any internal railroad in the western half of the factory without exceeding safe gradients. Consequently, the smaller jobs, like fuze and detonator manufacture, had to be put on the western side of the site, although this did not remove all the transport difficulties within the factory. There was no railway to the Clothing Stores (Building 10C30) in the southern section of the site since the London Midland and Scottish Railway Company (LMS) was not prepared to build sidings on both sides of its line.

By the end of July 1937 there were 1,928 construction workers on site, but due to the site difficulties mentioned above, combined with design alteration, completion had already slipped to March 1939. Permission was given to speed up construction by increasing the workforce so that by 13 October the workforce had risen to 3,984.[26] Delays continued due to construction difficulties and by February 1938 this figure had risen to 6,354 to compensate, of whom 2,120 were recruited locally from the North West.[27] As the workforce rose so did the amount spent per week, from £18,245 in July 1937 to £46,800 in October 1937. Continuing construction problems, combined with constant changes to the design of the

One of two large models of the factory, with group numbers added. These were used to help orientate new starters and visitors to the site.

factory, meant that work was again behind schedule by April 1938, when overtime, night shift and weekend working, were instituted.[28] The Munich crisis in autumn 1938, when it seemed likely that Britain and France would go to war against Germany over the future of Czechoslovakia, led to an order on 13 September 1938 to complete the factory in the minimum possible time, using temporary methods of construction if possible. The revised target was to have the 250 most advanced buildings, largely explosive filling buildings, ready for use on 1 December.[29] As the crisis deepened, troops were deployed to protect the site (on 4 October 1938)[30] and in the middle of November it was decided to transfer an initial core staff of a few dozen from Woolwich Arsenal to prepare those buildings which were completed for production, which began in a small way on 14 December. Thereafter buildings came into use as and when they were finished and there was a steady recruitment of filling staff, roughly 100 personnel a week in early 1939. The chief difficulty in this period was to find a sufficiently large administrative and instructional staff, as staffing

Plate 2.2 (ref 567). Taken in May 1938, this photograph shows construction of the wall and main gatehouse into the factory, located in Euxton Lane. Also visible to the right, through the wall, are the MoD Police Offices. In the centre distance, the South Side canteen steelwork can be seen under construction.

Plate 2.3 (ref 2.6). This view of Group 5 was taken in September 1938. It shows Cordite magazines under construction with rail access. The view is looking west towards Central Road, which crosses from left to right in the distance. The 'deep' magazines are off the photograph to the right.

numbers rose six fold in the first six months of 1939, and by 1941 had risen to over 35,000.[31]

Whilst production had begun in a limited way construction had not ended. At the end of December 1938, when construction peaked, over 14,000 workers were employed on the site, but the beginning of production delayed completion of the factory even further so that it was now postponed to June 1939.[32] Most of the buildings on the site had been completed by March 1939 and on 13 April it was decided to hurry the finishing by handing over most of the site to Royal Ordnance Factory staff who would complete the remaining details. This did, however, cost an extra £10,000.[33] Unfortunately, deficiencies in the construction techniques used were discovered by R O F staff, delaying completion further. When war was declared on 3 September 1939 there were still 40 buildings uncompleted on which HMOW was working, and the factory was far from being ready for full production.

The opening of the factory

With the beginning of production and the winding down of the construction programme in early 1939 it was decided to celebrate what was an immense engineering feat and which at the time was described as the greatest civil engineering project ever undertaken. A royal opening was arranged for the factory on 31 March 1939 by King George VI.[34] (Such morale-boosting visits were not unfamiliar to the construction workers at Chorley.[35] In August 1938 a gala had been held for the workers in the fields of Lisieux Hall in Dawson Lane to celebrate the amount of work already completed on the site.) The royal train arrived at ROF Halt at 9.45am and the King was given a tour of the whole site, by foot, car and rail. Like many before and since the King expressed surprise at the size of the factory.

By the time the construction of ROF Chorley was completed at the end of 1939, over 30 million bricks had been laid, 3 million

Plate 2.4 (ref 2.7). Construction of the 'deep' magazines necessitated a huge amount of soil removal. Some idea of the scale of this work can be seen in this December 1938 view. It shows mag. X9 under construction, at that time on group 6, later, Group 8. The concrete mag. is finished, and has yet to be covered with 50 feet of soil.

cubic yards of earth had been excavated, 1 million cubic yards of concrete used, 500,000 yards of steel fabric reinforcement erected, 10,000 yards of structural steel girders, 15,000 steel window frames and 300,000 square yards of glass used in the building construction. Fifty miles of roads and cleanways had been built along with 25 miles of railway track. Furthermore, the world's largest concrete mixer had been built at a cost of £30,000. This monster was 120 feet high and turned out 5,000 tons of concrete a day, with roughly 30 trains and 300 lorries needed to transport it to various points across the site.[36]

Early factory life and organisation

As early as 1936, government departments were discussing the probable staffing levels that would be required for the proposed new ROFs.[37] The staff to be moved were referred to as 'Pivotal', and were to be recruited mainly from the Royal Arsenal at

Plate 2.5 (ref 2.8). By 1939, the year King George VI officially opened the factory, work in many areas of the factory site was largely finished, yet work still continued on mounding over the deep magazines to the left. In the foreground, 'Avenue P' and its rail access to smaller mags, with their 'mounding', is completed.

Woolwich. In the first drafts of staff to work in the production areas at Chorley, which were determined in early 1938, the total number for transfer was 472, from superintendent to overlooker grade. A further five, including one Air Raid Warden, were also considered. Additionally, non-supervisory grades for work in the services area required 87 mechanics/electricians, 54 builders, 32 in steam/electricity generation, and 17 in transport – an extra 190 in total. A proviso attached to this provisional list said that if grass cutting was to be done by staff at Chorley, then a further 60 people would be needed. Clerical staff were estimated at 70. This made a grand total of 797. Surprisingly these estimates seem to have been fairly accurate, with slight changes to numbers in only one department. In January 1939 the previous list had been amended to 753. Actual figures of persons employed at ROF Chorley in June 1939 were: Superintendent 1, Production staff 521, Services Staff 156, Clerical 65, making a total of 743.[38] On top of this figure, 2 Danger Building Inspectors, 2 Doctors, 54

Plate 2.6 (ref 2.9). This view, taken on Group 3, 'D' Lines, shows the depth of excavation necessary when very wet areas were to be built upon, in this case the site of a pond. Note the men digging holes centre left, and the narrow gauge railway with locomotive, centre top. The date is August 1939.

Plate 2.7 (ref 2.11). Taken on 1 December 1939, this view shows the near-completed shifting house '1M1', located on Group 1. Not used as a shifting house since the end of the war, this building has been used by tradesmen etc. Note the old 'Riley' car, no doubt a collectable item today!

Police and one ARP Warden were required, bringing the total to 802.

The first 62 process workers to start at ROF Chorley were transferred from Woolwich Arsenal during the summer of 1938 to provide a nucleus of experience and expertise at the new factory. Some of them were present at the Opening Gala held adjacent to the factory in August 1938,[39] when Gracie Fields, the guest celebrity, is alleged to have sung perhaps her most famous song 'The Biggest Aspidistra in the World'.[40] The first shell was not filled until 3 p.m. on 4 December 1938.[41] This feat was recalled by one of the original Woolwich process workers, James Brown. The shell was a 3.7" MKID ack-ack with a 117 fuze which was filled at the same time. As soon as the filling was completed a telex was sent to the Ministry of Defence in London stating 'ROF Chorley now in production'.[42]

Senior staff had been transferred from Woolwich even earlier, to assist with the final work of installing process machinery. Lists showing industrial staff to be transferred to Chorley from

27

Woolwich detail not only the names of those to be moved with their personal details, such as dates of birth, but show their Woolwich rates of pay as well. For 47 hours work the lowest rate was £2 19s. 8d., and the highest £4 14s. 7d. At Chorley, many of these jobs were paid at a lower rate, which may have been one of the factors which deterred the Woolwich men from coming to Chorley, despite the offer of a re-location allowance to off-set the lower rates of pay,[43] ranging from £5 to £20 depending on annual salary.

As more local people were started at the factory to work along-side the Woolwich staff during 1939 and 1940, problems arose. New employees were not set to work initially with explosives. Rather, they were put into incoming component warehouses and stores, so that gradually they could become used to the way in which things were to be done if they were to become process workers. The problem of balancing the workforce with the work during 1939 and 1940 was a result early in the war of the inconsistent flow of empty components into the factory. This not only caused problems with the schedules for the filling of the munitions (as explosive munitions were called) but it often meant that men in the receiving storehouses had no work to do. As more shops were finished, ready for production work to start, a gradual steady increase of new staff was necessary. But often they had to be moved to different locations within the factory to keep them gainfully employed.[44]

Although the recruitment of new employees was a straight-forward operation, the number of interviewees was almost double the number of those taken on to work at the factory. This was because the men were not physically fit, and the huge majority of those interviewed had not held a steady job for some time.[45]

Many of the men who were given a start were, after a short time, found to be unsuitable for the job. This was often due to their flouting of factory rules, especially if working in the 'danger area' where the filling of ammunition was going on. The reliability of many new employees was another problem; they just did not turn up in time to catch their train or bus. At one period in 1940 almost as many were being dismissed weekly as were started. This turnover of staff and the problems with supply of components certainly caused many problems in the first year of production.

Plate 2.8 (ref B311/25). Shell filling on Group 6 was the first production accomplished at ROF Chorley in 1939. At that time, the fuzes for the shells were filled in the same shops. Later, Group 3 was completed to be used for fuze assembly. Here we see one of the fuze assembly shops, where filling was carried out by hand on compartmented benches.

From the outbreak of the war in September 1939, women were employed at ROF Chorley. They worked in all of the filling areas from powder mixing, fusz and tracer filling, to cordite charge manufacture and shell filling. At that time, shells were all filled by pouring the explosive mixture in by hand. They were also subject to all the health problems associated with exposure to explosive compositions, especially when working with TNT which caused anaemia, gastritis and toxic jaundice. Another of the compositions, Composition Explosive (CE), caused the skin to turn yellow along with the overalls and even underclothes. Dermatitis was another common skin problem which occurred when handling of chemical agents and cleansers. etc., despite the availability of protection creams, special soaps and gloves.

Factory medical staff and the Process Research departments strove to reduce toxic hazards through better medical prevention and working practices. The resultant improved conditions meant that 'less than 100 per cent fit' persons could be taken on, thus allowing the workforce requirements to be met more easily.

The effect of safety improvements made in the handling of explosive mixtures, and the many other agents required during the filling and assembly process at Chorley, can be seen in the

29

figures from the medical department. In 1942, there were 1,700 cases related to the effects of working with TNT and CE, but by 1944 this figure had fallen to 260. By 1945 the figure had been further reduced to 70 cases.

As the civil engineering work upon the explosive groups drew to an end in 1940, and the general infrastructure of the factory was completed, the full impact of the group system was felt by the new employees most obviously in the strictly controlled access to the groups. Because of the need to understand how the whole system worked, training courses were introduced during 1940, and ultimately led to the production of a staff hand book.

The factory had two 'sides': 'clean' and 'dirty'.[46] The dirty side was any area outside an explosives filling group, the explosive group itself being 'clean'. Within all groups there were areas which had partially 'dirty' workshops, used by services personnel such as fitters and joiners. There was a door which led to the 'dirty side' so that items required for maintenance work could be brought onto the group, or for machinery to be repaired going off the group. In the case of the latter, a 'Free From Explosives Certificate' had to go with the item to be repaired, after it had been checked as clear. The workshops had a barrier in them, separating the dirty side from the clean side.

For personnel to gain access to an explosives filling group it was necessary to enter the group via a changing room or Shift House, usually referred to as a 'Shifting House'. Upon entering the shifting house, workers would proceed to their respective bays, where outside clothes would be taken off and overalls put on. Personal effects were also removed. The overalls had no buttons and were secured by ribbon tapes. The reason for the absence of buttons was the risk that they might come off and fall into a store being filled with explosives. In inclement weather, woollen waistcoats (equivalent to the modern body warmer) were used over the overalls. Capes were supplied for wet weather. The women wore turbans, and the men wore small pill box type hats made of wool. Shoes were removed and special anti-static shoes put on, to lessen the risk of sparks being created within an explosives filling shop.

Once the workers had changed, they then proceeded to the 'clean' end of the shifting house. Here one of the group staff

Plate 2.9 (ref B108/5). During the war years when some 35,000 were employed at the factory, inter-group rivalry was promoted in order to achieve better output, better attendance, cleaner workshops etc. Annual awards were given for such activities. Here we see such an award being made in 1943. This was in canteen '6A3'. The stage has its customary piano, complete with notice saying 'not to be moved'!

would vet their attire before allowing them to step over a low barrier into the 'clean side'. Each worker would test himself or herself on an anti-static tester to ensure that they were safe. At this point they might be subjected to a search to ensure that they were not taking any forbidden items into the filling area. Searches were carried out at random on all the explosive groups to ensure that the safety rules were not breached. Once over the low barrier, a large red sign would remind workers of those articles which they were forbidden to take into the 'CLEAN SIDE':

The Following must not be taken onto the CLEAN SIDE.

MATCHES ... spent or unspent, or any means of producing light.

TOBACCO ... in any form, including snuff.

PIPE ... cigarette or any article connected with smoking.

FOOD ... sweetmeat, beverage or medicine.

PRIVATE BAG ... parcel, or bicycle equipment.

STICK ... or umbrella.

31

Plate 2.10 (ref B329/1). A washroom, known as 'ablution' in ROF parlance, had separate male/female buildings, although some were communal. They were great places for the gossips and rumourmongers. The large circular sinks had a multi-spray system, allowing workers to stand all around them to wash. The 'ablutions' also offered them special hand creams and soaps to avoid skin disorders such as dermatitis.

CHEMICAL OR EXPLOSIVE … or other obviously dangerous
articles.

KNIFE, SCISSORS, FILE, or any other sharp implement.

Having passed through the shifting house, each worker was able to proceed to their place of work, which in some cases was a ten minute walk away. Then they would remove their coat/cape and sign their name on a clipboard sheet, and then retest themselves on an anti-static meter. They could then enter their work place.

A visitor to an explosive group, on arrival at the shifting house, would be required to change into 'clean side' shoes, or to put

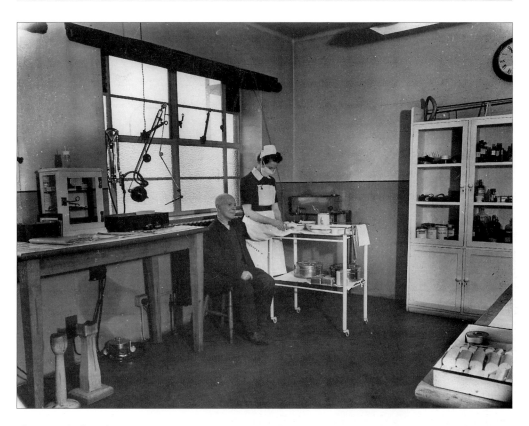

Plate 2.11 (ref 3.11). Each of the explosive filling groups at ROF Chorley had its own 'surgery', staffed by a qualified nurse. In addition to these, Main Surgery was located near the main gate into the factory, in Euxton Lane. Main Surgery had a doctor and staff, with facilities such as x-ray and an operating theatre. This 1944 photograph shows a rather spartan treatment room.

on overshoes. These did not have the same static inhibiting properties as did the proper shoes. The visitor would be expected to be wearing suitable clothing for access to the group, although not to the same degree as a process worker. The visitor would be asked if he or she had any 'contraband items' (i.e. those listed on the red sign outside cleanside), after which the visitor would sign in stating what their business was on the group, who they were seeing, and in which filling shop or other building. On returning to the shifting house after their visit, he or she would change into dirty side shoes, collect their contraband items and sign out.

The inspection of the munitions being filled and assembled, was done through a system of monitoring whereby regular visits were made to the shops to examine randomly selected items during assembly. A complete record of their findings was kept in a book. If all was found to be satisfactory work would continue at the same rate, with monitor checks being made at intervals.

If anomalies were found, then corrections were made and the monitor checks would take place at more regular intervals, to ensure that the product, which was made in specified quantities, or 'Lots', was being correctly assembled.

The 'Lotting and Batching' of explosive stores was complicated, in that sub-assemblies had their own 'lot' number, as had the main assembly into which the sub-assemblies would be fitted. Usually, the lot number of the store was based on the full round, not the sub-assembly. But this was not the case with every store produced.

The X-ray Department was responsible for the x-raying of all filled sub-assemblies and finally the assembled munitions. The department had many special facilities on the explosive groups for producing photographs of the sub- and main assemblies. In many cases, as on Groups 2 and 3, the x-ray facility was integral to the production shops. Here sub-assemblies, such as fuzes and

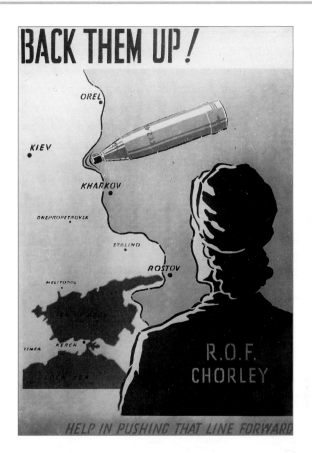

pellets, could be scanned immediately for either 'foreign bodies' or voids. On Group 6, where shells were filled, the main purpose of x-raying the filled shell was to determine whether the explosive filling was without voids or cavities, and was homogeneous. This was particularly important due to the hand filling operations that were done. Any cavity within a filled shell can, if fired from a gun, cause a premature explosion of the shell, due to the adiabatic expansion of the air in any cavity, and the heat being generated therein.

Movement of sub-assemblies between groups was done mostly by using a dilly, a small electrically powered vehicle. External transport on the dirty side would take the components to other groups, to the main bulk magazines, or to a suitable railway wagon loading platform ready to be moved to the marshalling yards. If groups were inter-connected by a 'cleanway', as all the paths of an explosive group area were called, the dilly with its loads could pass between groups. The only group not to utilise the dilly for movement of components was Group 1, where sensitive compositions were made and carried between workshops by hand. The carriers of sensitive compositions and/or detonators were not allowed to walk together, nor were they allowed to be accompanied by non-carriers. On arrival at their shop destination, the boxes of explosives were not taken into the shop via the door, but were placed in hatches in the outside wall of the shop until required.

On the shell group, a separate system from the dilly was used on the filling lines, where, during the course of one day, a large number of both empty and filled shells were moved. Here another small electric truck was used to move the shells in and out of the press lines.[47]

The end of the beginning

The problems with the factory, its construction and organisation were neatly summarised in a memo from Dr A Jacques, the Chorley factory superintendent, to Mr Newton-Booth at Woolwich Arsenal on 24 June 1939; 'The deficiencies may be due to a number of causes: lack of information by the OF of the requirements it was to meet: failure on the part of RFF to specify the facilities required: or on the part of ED (F) to carry them out: failure on the part of HMOW to provide exactly what it had been asked to provide'.[48]

Despite these problems when war was declared, Group 6, roughly one quarter of Royal Ordnance Factory Chorley, was ready to produce the finished cartridges, shells, and high explosive bombs that the army, navy and air force would need in the forthcoming struggle.

CHAPTER THREE

Chorley During the Second World War

Chorley and the Second World War

Whilst Chorley had been handed over to the Royal Ordnance in April 1939, only a quarter of the factory was in production at the outbreak of war in September of that year, and it was not until well into 1940 that full production was possible. Chorley had been built specifically for a conflict such as this, and the years 1940 to 1945 saw the filling factory used to its absolute capacity. This period marks the culmination of the plans suggested in December 1934 and provides an heroic chapter in Chorley's history. In order to understand Chorley's role in this conflict as the largest filling factory in Royal Ordnance, employing at its height a workforce of around 35,000, accounting for about ten per cent of the total workforce then working for the Royal Ordnance factories in 1943,[1] it is necessary briefly to review the course of the war, and the impact of changing military needs on the role of Chorley.

It was fortunate that Britain's declaration of war was followed by a long period of inactivity, known as the Phoney War. The British Expeditionary Force (BEF) was despatched to France but the defensive strategy adopted meant that both armies stayed behind the fortified line in north-eastern France known as the Maginot Line, whilst in the air neither the Allies nor Germany were willing to begin bombing each other. Poland was conquered in September 1939 without any allied intervention and the Phoney War only ended with the German invasion of Norway on 10 April 1940. By this time Chorley was close to full production and by the end of that year a further seven of the newly commissioned

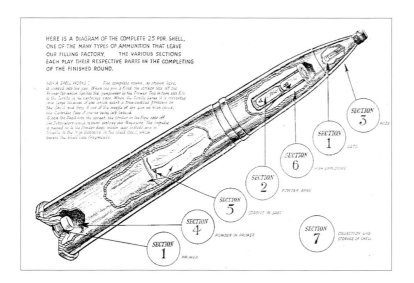

HERE IS A DIAGRAM OF THE COMPLETE 25 PDR. SHELL,
ONE OF THE MANY TYPES OF AMMUNITION THAT LEAVE
OUR FILLING FACTORY.   THE VARIOUS SECTIONS
EACH PLAY THEIR RESPECTIVE PARTS IN THE COMPLETING
OF THE FINISHED ROUND.

factories were operational. Royal Ordnance production at this stage was concentrated on the production of munitions for defence rather than offence, with the emphasis on re-equipping the army.[2]

There followed a series of defeats that left Britain isolated and on the verge of defeat. Denmark was occupied in April 1940 and Norway was conquered by 10 June. The failure of British troops and the British Navy to stop the conquest of Norway led to the fall of the Conservative government under Neville Chamberlain, who resigned on 10 May. He was replaced as Prime Minister by Winston Churchill, leading an all-party coalition.[3] The Blitzkrieg campaign of May and June 1940 saw German armed forces sweep across western Europe invading the Netherlands, Belgium and France. The Netherlands capitulated on 15 May and Belgium on the 28th. The surrender of Belgium and the German attack through the Ardennes towards the English Channel threatened to encircle the BEF, who had moved northwards to engage the Germans in Belgium. Around 335,000 British, French and Belgian soldiers were rescued from the beaches of Dunkirk at the beginning of June, though most of their equipment was lost. France finally surrendered on 22 June 1940.[4]

The Battle of Britain during August and September 1940 secured Britain against the imminent threat of invasion and allowed the re-equipping of the British Army to begin. This could

MEET **Freddie** THE PERFECT FILLER!

HE IS HERE AS A FRIEND TO
HELP YOU. LET HIS EXPERIENCE
BE YOUR GUIDE. TAKE HIS ADVICE.
HE KNOWS THIS FILLING JOB
FROM A TO Z.
SO READ CAREFULLY ALL THAT
FREDDIE HAS TO SAY —
YOU'LL FIND IT WELL WORTH WHILE!

'Freddie the Perfect Filler' explained to employees the correct techniques for the various filling processes. His alter ego, Calamity Claude, demonstrated the pitfalls awaiting those who ignored correct procedures.

not have been achieved, however, without the creation of an efficient distribution system. Traditionally the supply of munitions, vehicles and other equipment for the military had been undertaken individually by the three armed services. In order to improve the speed of supply this system was taken over by the newly created Ministry of Supply. Its first duty was to improve the distribution network for the army. Since Chorley was envisaged as supplying mainly the army, the factory was brought into this new system at this stage. By May 1940 the supply for the Royal Air Force was formalised under this Ministry through the new Minister for Aircraft Production. The Royal Navy had always had its own supply system and retained control of this throughout the war.[5] The efficiency of Britain's supply and distribution network was a key factor in winning the war. It enabled factories like Chorley to work twenty-four hours a day throughout the year with minimal interruptions. In contrast, production at German munitions factories was increasingly disrupted. Firstly through the allied bombing campaign from 1943 onwards, and,

39

secondly, through the progressive destruction of the railway and road network.

The end of the Battle of Britain also marked the beginning of the globalisation of the conflict and, as far as Britain and in particular ROF Chorley were concerned, a renewed emphasis on the aerial conflict, especially the night-time bombing of military and industrial targets in Germany, which began in October 1940.[6] It was in late 1940 and early 1941[7] that bomb filling was returned to Chorley, being located in Group 6 along with shell filling. Bomb filling had originally been part of Chorley's remit, but had been transferred to Glascoed in 1938 before this part of the site had been completed. There were three types of major battle-winning bombs during the Second World War (excluding those

The Railway System

The factory had its own internal railway system from the beginning. Access to this was from the London, Midland and Scottish Railway, the LMS, with whom negotiations for factory sidings and a station (ROF Halt) were entered into during 1937. The station was a busy place, with some forty trains a day setting down or picking up employee passengers only. The trains carried workers to and from all parts of Lancashire; from Manchester, Lancaster, Blackpool and Burnley. As well as the access steps to the station platforms from the Central Road viaduct at the western end, a footbridge was built at the eastern end of the platforms to allow access to the administrative block and Group 6, the footbridge to the group passing over the factory marshalling yard.

Access to the factory railway system was from a sidings complex west of the viaduct. In these sidings ammunition trains were made up by the factory's own steam (later diesel) locomotives, to be collected by the locomotives of the railway company, for transit to ammunition depots throughout the country. Trains coming into the ROF sidings brought empty components, such as brass cartridge cases, shell bodies and a host of other sub-assemblies.

The factory's first locomotives were steam powered, being loaned by the civil contractor responsible for the building of the factory. One of these was allegedly a very old steam locomotive, having no cab to protect the driver/fireman from the elements; a cab was fitted soon after its arrival. This old locomotive was named *Hannah* and spent most of its life moving trains of coal from the sidings up to the four boiler houses of the factory located on Groups 1, 4N and 5. The steam locomotives which worked the factory were made by Barclays of Kilmarnock, and two of these were named *Marlborough* and *Fisher*.

ROF Chorley had approximately twenty miles of track, most of which was located east of Central Road. The only place where the railway passed over to the western side of the road was where a branch line ran to the loco shed and sidings in the service workshops and to a separate small burning ground, passing *en route* the boiler house on Group 1.

types developed for specific purposes); these were the incendiary, and the medium- and high-capacity explosive bombs.[8]

The new bomb facility at Chorley covered all these types, from incendiaries and small to medium general purpose bombs of 40lbs to 4,000lbs, to the medium- and high-capacity bombs which ranged in size from 500lbs to the 12,000lb Tallboy bombs.[9] Chorley also helped in the development of one-off, specialist bombs, and in 1943 the factory is reputed to have filled the bouncing bombs designed by Barnes Wallis, the 9,150lb Upkeep (strictly speaking being a mine). According to some former wartime employees, over fifty of the bouncing bombs were filled at Chorley on Group 8.[10] These were used in May 1943 for the night-time attack on the dams of the River Ruhr which supplied hydro-electricity for the main industrial complex of the Ruhr valley in Germany.[11]

From the beginning of the European war in 1939 the United States had supported Britain on an informal basis. In November 1940, after Roosevelt had been re-elected as president, more formal

Plate 3.1 (ref 3.15). Empty shells came into ROF Chorley from the 'empty manufacturers', usually one of the other 'engineering ROFs'. They came to the factory by road and rail. On the factory they were received on Group 6 (later Group 8) in one of the 'transit buildings'. The plate shows shells in building B18 in 1941.

Plate 3.2 (ref 3.17). When received in the transit buildings, the empty shells were sorted, temporarily stacked, cleaned, and then issued to the filling shops. This photograph shows shells on roller conveyors, in the process of being cleaned.

cooperation began with the establishment of the Defence Advisory Committee between the United States and Britain. This was followed in May 1941 by the Lend-Lease Act which empowered the President to supply war materials to 'any country whose defence the President deems vital to the defence of the United States'. Of key importance to the British war effort was that these war materials did not need to be paid for immediately. After the Japanese attack on Pearl Harbor on 7 December 1941 the United States declared war not only on Japan (8 December) but also on Germany and Italy (11 December). Shortly afterwards the British and the United States military staff began talks on joint military actions and a combined strategy. The first extensive joint military operations began in 1942 with the invasion of North Africa and the beginning of the British and American night-time aerial bombardment of German war industries and German urban civilian populations with incendiary and high-explosive bombs.[12] In 1943 day-time raids by large groups of bombers began on German centres of industry. However, in 1943 preparations began for invasion of western Europe in 1944 and the ultimate liberation of Europe. Whilst large scale bombing raids on the German transport network did continue throughout 1944 and into early 1945, at Chorley the emphasis was once more on shell filling and small calibre ammunition for the European invasion force.

The organisation of the factory

The success of ROF Chorley during the war can be attributed to two things: the efficient organisation of the factory through the group system, which allowed the free flow of munitions around the site in as safe a manner as possible; and the commitment of the workforce (which numbered around 35,000 by 1942),[13] who worked three shifts a day to allow 24-hour working.

The group system had always been at the core of the new filling factory. It had been developed at Woolwich Arsenal in the early

Plate 3.3 (ref 3.16). Another view in the same building as the previous plate. Here we see shells in the process of being cleaned by hand on benches. A large number were employed here because of all the heavy work associated with manhandling the shells. Note also the shell 'bays', stating calibres: '5.8 & 9.2 Howitzers'; and '4.5, 5.5 & 8 inch gun'.

Plate 3.4 (ref 3.10). During the war years, shell filling was done by hand, pouring the explosives from 'kettles'. These were kept hot by a steam jacket, which ensured the explosive composition was kept in a molten state. The photograph shows explosive composition being poured into shells.

twentieth century, partly as a way of ensuring safety during munitions production, and partly to speed up the production process itself.[14] The earliest plan of the site to survive, dated 1 October 1937, envisaged seven groups, with the factory divided by a main road running north to south known as Central Road. The western half of the site was the location of sub-assembly munitions facilities, and the eastern half of the site was where munitions assembly and storage was to be. In the west, Group 1 was to be the location of cap and detonator production; Group 2 for pellet and powder bag production; and Group 3 for fuze production. In the east, Group 4 was to be used for General Purpose (GP) filling; Group 5 was to be the cordite assembly and cartridge filling facility for the small calibre Quick Fire (QF) ammunition; Group 6 for High Explosive (HE) filling of bombs and shells; whilst Group 7 marked the end of the production process where the filled shells and ammunition were stored. Management of the explosive groups was referred to as east side or west side. The two sides of the factory were sub-divided again to give east side north, which included Groups 4 North and Group 5. East side south, included the Groups 6, 7 and 4 South. West side north, to the west side of Central Road, included

45

Groups 2 and 3, the Proof Yard and Burning Ground, whilst west side south included the services area and Group 1. The service area was in fact in the centre of the site alongside the Central Road. Here fitting and machine shops, electricians shops, Process Research, garage, locomotive shed, joiners shop, pipe shop and laundry were located.

Since navigating around 928 acres, seven groups and 1500 buildings could become very disorientating, two further measures were taken to ease the flow of materials and people around the site. Firstly, all roads running north to south were given the name 'Street 1–2–3' etc, whilst the roads running east to west were given the name 'Avenue A-B-C' etc. Secondly, every building had its own unique number; even the toilets and washrooms were numbered and lettered. This comprised three parts; the first being the Group number, the second being a letter denoting a series of buildings forming a line within the group, and the third the number of the building within that line, e.g. 5 (Group) E (line)

Plate 3.5 (ref 3.50). Production of 25-pounder shells in 1943. The shells are filled and are being fitted with paper/felt washers etc., and a plug, which takes the place of the fuze during the production sequence. The fuze will be fitted later, prior to issue of the shells.

Plate 3.6 (ref Big Bomb). ROF Chorley filled many of the 'big bombs' used by the RAF in the war. Like other bombs, these too were filled by hand. This photograph shows bomb production in progress on Group 6 'C' Lines. The bomb 'body' is some six feet long by almost three feet in diameter. In this scene the explosive composition in the bomb is being stirred. These bombs were referred to as 'Blockbusters'.

Plate 3.6a (ref B223/10). The 'Big Bombs' were filled with liquid explosive composition close to the 'Incorporators', which heated and mixed the explosive. Added to the liquid explosive, and thoroughly mixed with it, was explosive 'biscuit'. The bombs were moved away on special trolleys, and allowed to cool down a little, after which the explosive was 'topped up' by hand, as seen in this photograph.

Plate 3.7 (ref 2.2). In this photograph, dated June 1941, 6" Howitzer shells are bing topped up with explosive composition around the exploder cavity. Behind the shells are large cylindrical chambers which housed presses to consolidate the explosive in the shell. These were called 'Queen Marys'.

11 (building). The group system at ROF Chorley, with its numbered buildings and roads, was also used at the other filling factories being built at Glascoed, Swynnerton and Thorp Arch.

What in effect amounted to a staff hand book from 1942/3 details how the site was organised.[15] The factory was divided into two sections: production, which covered most of the site and lay to the north of the London, Midland & Scottish (LMS) railway, and administration in a separate area south of the railway. The production side, being the primary function of the site, was huge with seven production sections (the groups), and a workforce of over 35,000 divided into five divisions known as Progress (ie production), Experimental, Development, Training and Inspection. The arrangement of the groups was similar to that envisaged in October 1937, with Groups 1 to 3 lying in the western half of the site and Groups 4 to 7 in the eastern part. The main difference was that Group 4 (which was on two sites on the fringes of the factory) now undertook the manufacture of the explosive powders needed for the shells, bombs and

Plate 3.8 (ref 2.1). Another view of manual shell filling using a 'kettle', taken in January 1944. Note the steam connections 'in' and 'out' on the 'kettle'. The explosive composition being poured into the shell is 'Pentolite'.

Plate 3.9 (ref 3.1). Every explosive composition had its own unique colour code, and containers were painted accordingly. This illustration shows a selection of waste containers, together with their codes. Even though the photograph is in black and white, the description enables us to distinguish different explosive container types. This illustration was originally a poster displayed throughout the factory.

ammunition. This task had been added to the design of the factory in 1938.

The production processes

The production process was associated with the layout of the factory and the group system, so that despite the variety of products made and filled at Chorley between 1939 and 1945

51

(from small calibre rounds to 12,000lb bombs), the actual production process was based upon common principles.

Production began at Group 1 where caps, primers and detonators were filled entirely by hand. The primer cap was a small copper shell filled with a special composition that was inserted at the base of each primer. The base of the primer comprised the QF (Quick Fire) cap, anvil, cone or pea-ball plug, and was topped by a paper disc. The magazine of the primer was filled with gunpowder and the completed component was sent to Group 5 to be screwed into the bottom of the cartridge case.

The detonator was a small copper shell filled with a very sensitive detonating composition. Special precautions were therefore necessary to prevent jarring or rubbing, and all filling operations were done behind specially tested screens. The filled detonators were cleaned, varnished, and dried before they were ready for shipping to Group 3, where they were inserted into the fuzes. These hand production processes remained largely unchanged until mechanisation in the late 1970s and mid 1980s.

Group 2 was dedicated to the manufacture of various sizes of

Plate 3.10 (3.19). Filled shells were fitted to their cartridge cases on Group 5 at Chorley. On this group, the propellant used in the case was cut to size, weighed and bundled. This photograph shows a group of ladies weighing and bundling cordite propellant. At the far end of the bench stands the only man on the photograph – the shop 'senior', who would have been either a 'greenband' or a 'blueband'. The lady standing, is 'on inspection'.

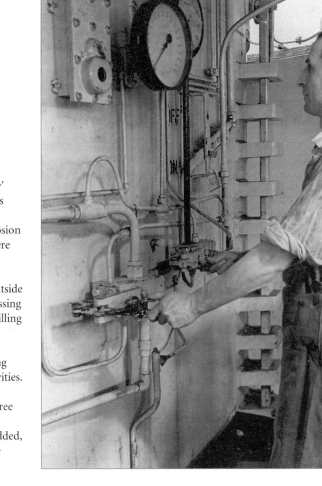

Plate 3.11 (3.4). The 'Queen Mary' pressing chambers were designed to contain any explosion that occurred. Here we see the press controls being operated from outside the chamber. Pressing of the explosive filling was done to 'consolidate' the explosive, ensuring there were no cavities. Filling sometimes needed two or three 'increments' of explosive to be added, each having to be pressed.

pellets and the filling of powder or exploder bags. The pellets were made of explosive powder such as CE (Composition Explosive) or TNT, and pressed at approximately three tons per square inch by a hydraulic press. They were then sent to Group 3 to be inserted into their own particular fuzes. The exploder bags were filled with CE or TNT and then sent to Group 6 for insertion into shells or bombs as part of the detonation process.

Fuzes, which were used to bring about the detonation of the main or bursting charge of shells and bombs, were the speciality

of Group 3. Here two types of fuzes were filled; percussion and time fuzes. The percussion fuze functioned on striking any object of sufficient resistance. The impact forced the strikers down on to the detonator which exploded, igniting a stemmed channel (filled with explosive) which culminated in the final bursting of the shell. Some shells and bombs were required to burst after a certain time, so a time, or delay, fuze was used.

The manufacture of fuze composition (the main ingredients of which were potassium nitrate, charcoal and sulphur) on Group 4 had been a late addition to the design of Chorley, and may partly explain why this group was located on the eastern fringes of the complex, away from the main assembly areas and filling groups. The use of gunpowder as a propellant had ceased by the end of the nineteenth century, but there was still a demand for fine-grained gunpowder as a fuze composition, for priming cordite, cartridges, picric powder, nitric acid, nitroglycerine, and guncotton in mines and torpedoes. During the First World War

Plate 3.12 (3.14). At the other end of the scale, the smallest 'press' operation was 'stemming'. The stemming operation was carried out by small machines which allowed small increments of 'composition' to fall from a hopper, to be consolidated by a small piston. Stemming operations were carried out mainly in fuze assembly shops, as with this photograph taken in shop 'G4' on Group 3.

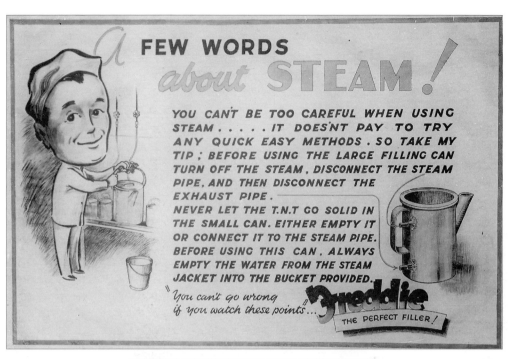

The Hostels

Many workers had been moved from distant places to come and work at the factory. Some of these were accommodated in lodgings in Chorley and Leyland. Many could not be found accommodation, and therefore temporary accommodation, in the form of hostels, had to be built. Throughout Britain, 48 hostels, 14 staff clubs and 7 guest houses were built for the Royal Ordnance factories by the Ministry of Supply.[26] At ROF Chorley a small housing estate had been built, which was used for some of the staff transferred from Woolwich Arsenal and for the Ministry of Defence police. Other guest workers were housed in purpose built hostels further away from the factory.[27]

There were three of these hostels, each designed to accommodate 2,000 people. Two of these were opened in 1942.[28] The first, Highways, was located on Balshaw Lane in Euxton adjoining a railway station. These hostels were at first glance similar to an army camp, being a little austere in appearance. Highways was, however, described by those who lived there as 'comfortable'. The hostel provided all of the moral and cultural requirements for those living in. It had shops, a library, a medical centre, a laundry, a dance hall with a regular band, recreation rooms and tennis courts. A staff of 90 was required to run Highways, some of them living there permanently. Although built by the Ministry of Supply, the hostel, like all the other hostels in the country, was managed by the National Service Hostel Association, who had the YWCA/YMCA organisations to run them. At Highways, the

running of the hostel was by the YWCA, for it was a women's hostel only.

The second hostel to be opened was Woodlands, and this was for men. Although having similar facilities, and run by the same joint committee, it did not have all that Highways had to offer; for example it had no dance hall. For board and lodgings, which included two meals a day during week days and three on a Sunday, the men paid £3 5s. 6d. per week and the women paid £3 1s. 6d. Most amenities were provided on site. Each person had their own room (although it was not very big), and meals, social functions and games were organised. Even events between the hostels were organised.

In between the two hostels described above, a third one was built. This was not used by ROF workers but was finished 'in readiness' should the need arise. It never did, and the hostel, which was unnamed, was empty for a time and was not staffed on a permanent basis. Hostel number three was taken over by the American forces (USAAF) in 1942 and named Washington Hall. The lane which ran along the north western boundary of the camp also had its name changed. This was hardly surprising for it was called German Lane, although it was named after one of the old families of the neighbourhood rather than the country. The new name given to the lane was quite a talking point in the Euxton hostelries at the time, particularly as it was only the northern end which passed alongside Washington Hall that was changed, the southern portion retaining its 'German' title.

Plate 3.13 (3.18). Many different types of fuzes were filled at ROF Chorley, the empty components coming mainly from ROF Blackburn. One type was a 'ime' fuze. This was made up from several (3 or 4) rings, which could be turned to set the 'burning time'. Each ring having a 'channel' filled with composition. The photograph shows a time fuze production shop.

the Royal Gunpowder Factory at Waltham Abbey was the sole manufacturer of fuze powders, but by the start of the Second World War most production was being undertaken by filling factories, such as that established at Chorley, and in 1943 the manufacture of fuze composition was completely taken over by these new type of factories.[16] Group 4 was divided into two sections; one part manufactured the fuze composition described above, which was used in the time fuzes produced by Group 3. In the second part production was confined to the making of various gunpowder pellets and the supplying of gunpowder to Group 1, where it was used in the filling of the primers.

The filling of the shells and bombs with high explosive was the task of Group 6. There were three methods of achieving this. Firstly, by melting the TNT and mixing it with a certain amount of ammonium nitrate. This formed a plastic mass called Amatol which was forced into the shell by means of an extruder, the machine used being known as a 'worm'. One shell was filled at a time, and the operation was performed behind the protection

57

of a thick steel-walled cubicle. The second method involved the melting of TNT or Amatol in steam-heated kettles and its pouring in the shells, where it was left to solidify. Thirdly, the 25lb shell has its own process whereby the shell was filled with cold, milled Amatol by a machine working on a conveyor belt. The filling was subsequently pressed into a solid block by means of a hydraulic press capable of handling up to 16 shells at once. Once the shells had been filled and pressed, pellets or exploder bags from Group 2 were inserted and the filled fuzes from Group 3 screwed into place.

The assembly of the munitions took place on the eastern half of the site. Group 5 received the filled shells from Group 6 and the primers from Group 1, and proceeded to complete the assembly of quick firing rounds of ammunition. An additional task was the filling of cartridge cases with cordite. Cordite (a propellant charge) was cut into specific lengths, weighed and tied into bundles. In some munitions, such as the 25lb shells, the cordite was sewn into bags before being put in the cartridge case,

Plate 3.14 (3.12). Empty and filled fuzes were moved between filling/assembly shops on small trailers pulled by an electric 'dilly'. The trailers contained fuzes stacked in trays, as shown here arriving inside one of the process shops on Group 3.

Canteens

At ROF Chorley there were 16 canteens and a further two or three small mess rooms which did not provide food. On the explosive filling groups there were 14 canteens, eight of these being two storey, indicating these were the areas where the biggest concentration of labour was engaged. The canteen staff were kept busy, they too having to work on the three shift system, preparing and serving food for around 35,000 people each day.

Although smoking was allowed in the canteens, the use of matches or lighters to light them was not. Instead, on the pillars supporting the canteens' roofs were special electric heaters into which a cigarette, held between the lips, could be inserted and lit.

The main canteen for the administrative building and storehouses, which incorporated a senior staff dining room, was to the south of the factory, away from the Danger Area. This had an adjoining bakery and a two-story section which served as an MOD police canteen and club. There was a large stage in the main part of the canteen and from here radio broadcasts were made to the country on several occasions during the war.

The large floor area of the main canteen, at South Side, was used for a number of other events. It was the venue for the popular wartime radio programme 'Workers Playtime' and it was also used for factory dances, at lunch times, and during weekends, for sporting activities, such as badminton, table tennis and snooker. The space also provided an indoor parade area for the MOD police, civil defence groups, and the factory's fire brigade.

The farmers and market gardeners of the local community did not profit greatly from the foodstuffs used in the canteens at ROF Chorley. The food used was supplied to the factory from official sources and was brought by road vehicles. Occasionally, local growers would be asked to supply items if there were shortages from the official source. In fact the farmers and growers did not seek to provide foodstuffs on a regular basis, due to the red tape required and the regular visits by the Ministry of Supply Inspectors this would involve. The Ministry of Supply controlled the canteens using a similar system to the NAAFI organisation; to accumulate no profit, yet incur no loss was their motto. Any profits which did arise were put back into the system for improvements. Despite this canteen provision many workers still brought in their own food. This practice was discouraged through the use of posters showing balanced meals, and more appetising ones than were being brought from home by the workers. The menus were made as interesting as possible, with as much variation as the rationing restrictions would allow.

whilst in the case of the 40mm and the 2lb shell it was put in the case and tied with a cord.

The final part of the process was Group 7, the storage magazines and distribution hub of the site. In 1942 this section dealt each week with approximately 1,100 trucks delivering components to site (including 500 tons of TNT, 350 tons of ammonium nitrate, and 170 tons of cordite). Each week between 750 and 800 truck loads of filled ammunition were dispatched from the site, including 210 truck loads of completed 25lb shells, and 70 truck loads of completed 5.5″ Howitzer shells.

Besides these core groups there were also a number of other areas. The Burning Ground was located between Groups 1 and 3 next to the Proof Yards. This was used for destroying the general waste and contaminated materials safely. Destruction was achieved by burning gas. For example, on Group 6, where shell filling was carried out, a large amount of TNT was used in 'biscuit' form. Much of this biscuit was surplus at the end of the filling process. It would then be regarded as contaminated and would have to be destroyed by burning.

The work of the Proof Yards was to prove or proof all of the munitions being filled at Chorley, not just to ensure that they

Plate 3.15 (3.13). Taken in June of 1943, the photograph shows a typical 'transit' store. This is Building 'H1' on Group 3. It was one of the buildings from which filled stores were despatched to other groups or out of the factory altogether. The 'full' condition of the store gives some idea as to quantity of fuzes being produced at the time.

performed as per specification, but to ensure that they were safe to be handled and transported. This proofing was done using a proven mathematical process, which allowed random selections to be taken which were representative of the lot or batch, being filled. The proof results showed whether or not it was necessary to take more or less for proof firing, thereby controlling the process of inspection of the munitions as well, being either tightened or relaxed. During the early years of the war, the proof yard saw less work than in the later years, due to the policy of getting as many products to the services as quickly as possible.

There was also the engineering services division which maintained the site (including the boiler houses and railway engines), and generally ensured that the factory was fit for production. They were based in the centre of the factory along the western side of Central Road.

The main building types

There were around 1,500 buildings at ROF Chorley, though many of these were not directly related to the production of munitions (such as ablution buildings, passive air defence buildings, canteens). The main building types associated with munitions production were the shifting houses, the filling buildings and the magazine stores.[17]

There were over 30 shifting houses within the factory. These were essentially changing rooms, and they provided the link between the clean and dirty sides of the complex. The name seems to have originated during the war years, when different shifts of workers used different bays in the buildings to change their clothes. There were separate shifting houses for men and women. There is another possible reason for the name. According to some of the former Woolwich staff, the name came from the 'old days' at Woolwich Arsenal, when overalls for the workers were a simple coverall garment, or a 'shift'.[18]

The process/filling buildings, the location for both sub-assembly and final assembly production of the munitions, were the most common buildings on the site. They were essentially long rectangular single storey blocks, designed to offer the least resistance to explosion and, thus, to minimise the danger of flying

61

debris. Each had its own lightning conductor. Nails and screws used in building construction were made from bronze, as were the fittings such as locks and hinges. This was to prevent the creation of accidental sparks and to ensure no sparks should occur in the event of a nail or screw falling into one of the machines. Filling buildings dominated the explosive groups within the danger area. Most of the lightweight buildings used were surrounded by earth embankments (traverses) to safeguard against accidents.

There were over 38 magazines built at Chorley, the designs of which were the culmination of decades of trial and error. In order to provide some protection against explosions, lightning conductors had been used in filling factories from the early nineteenth century onwards, whilst brick and earth traverses were introduced around buildings from the late nineteenth century. At ROF Chorley there were two types of magazine: small buildings used as transit magazines which could be found all over the site; and large or deep magazines which were mounded and were used for

Plate 3.16 (3.51). The illustrators department (based in the Training Centre) was responsible for the production of posters which dealt with a wide range of topics, including safety, filling, and group productivity figures, but above all they encouraged the workforce to 'support the fighting forces'.

Plate 3.17 (ref B/39/1). As well as shells and bombs many other types of munitions were produced at ROF Chorley. In this view, which dates from 1943, anti-tank mines are being pour-filled with liquid TNT explosive. 'biscuit explosive' was also used in these mines. Like many filling shops there was a limit on the number of personnel permitted to work in the shop at any one time. In this case only three were allowed and thus the women in the picture are numbered one to three.

the long term storage of munitions. These were confined to Groups 5 and 6. Both the processing buildings and the magazines were constructed so as to minimise the impact of explosions by either containment, as with magazines, or to offer the least resistance, as with the filling buildings which had a wooden felted roof to allow any blast to escape upwards rather than sideways. By contrast the shifting houses had concrete roofs to protect the employees, for these were non-process buildings.

Factory life and the local community

During the war years, the men and women forming the workforce within the ROFs worked towards one goal; to supply the services with the munitions and other equipment needed to defend the country. Despite the long hours and anti-social shift working, or air raids in many parts of the country, their efforts to supply the fighting forces with as much as it was possible to give went a long way to bringing the war to an end.

Details of wages at ROF Chorley during the war years are

sparse. One of the difficulties in determining the rates of pay was that there were so many grades among the workforce, from the skilled men of the services departments to workers on the explosive filling groups. Drawing parallels with the general wage rates as paid during the early 1940s, a wage of £10 per week was high. Former employees, who worked at the factory during the war years, recalled a wage of about £5 as being the basic amount. On top of this was the collective bonus, which could be as high as £2 to £3 per week. In addition there was a small allowance for

Plate 3.18 (ref G 7157). Although produced by ROF Chorley's Senior Illustrator, John Stanley, in the early 1950s, this painted mural embodies many of the filling and assembly processes as used in wartime, such

as pellet pressing, shell filling, detonator filling and fuze assembly. The mural also shows some of the factory buildings and the 'cleanway' bridges over roads.

working on shifts. Thus a wage of between eight to nine pounds, less deductions, would give a take home pay of perhaps £7 only.

A large proportion of the workforce who came to the Chorley factory in 1939 and 1940 were unskilled. The men came from a general labouring background, largely within the building trades, cotton mills or coal mines. The women came largely from the cotton mills of the district and from those mill towns on the eastern side of the county (Blackburn, Burnley, Colne and Darwen) where many of the mills had closed down due to a

65

shortage of raw material.[19] This largely unskilled workforce came to work within a factory where at least semi-skilled status was necessary. They were to handle explosive materials, and had to be aware of the dangers inherent in this work.[20]

New starters at ROF Chorley needed, as quickly as possible, to become fully aware of the dangers to themselves and others whilst working with explosives, so this was stressed from their first day. The first morning of their employment was spent at a series of lectures, and reading booklets showing the do's and don'ts of what their work would entail. The 'Rules of the Danger Area' were read to the new starters, and explanations were given about workshops, and what could or could not be contained within them. In many cases specific job instructions were positioned alongside the working station, so that, provided they followed those instructions to the letter, they would be working correctly and safely. Even so, many employees flouted the regulations from the very beginning. They used incorrect tools for the job, such as using ferrous instead of non-ferrous tools. They carried forbidden items onto the 'cleanside' and used sticks of TNT as chalk. Some were even caught smoking on explosives groups!

Gradually the length of the training period for new starters was extended in an effort to instill into them that the rules had to be followed. The first full day's training course started in 1941, about the same time as three shift working began. Two shift working had been in place since 1940, when the factory was completed.

No doubt the terminology and the abbreviations used were another area which caused the new starter confusion. Every workshop and filling shop had its own instructions. These were called simply SSIs (Superintendent's Safety Instructions) and were in several parts, all of which were stating what was to be done in that particular shop, which tools had to be used, and what the explosive limits of the building were. In 1939 the only legislation covering explosive working was the 1875 Explosives Act. This had been amended in 1937 to cover the many necessary processes and working conditions in an explosives factory. In July 1939 the Act was amended again, to incorporate more new legislation covering ablutions and correct clothing, both of which were

Now, about POURING!

WHEN FILLING, SUPPORT THE SPOUT OF THE CAN WITH SPONGE CLOTH, AND REMEMBER TO WIPE OFF THE LAST DROP EACH TIME YOU FINISH. DONT, ON ANY ACCOUNT, REST THE SPOUT ON THE LIP OF THE SHELL OR FILLING SOCKET.

WHEN USING THE GAUGE OR BREAKING-DOWN ROD AT THE SAME TIME, BE SURE THAT THE LAST DROP OF T.N.T. GOES INTO THE SHELL, BEFORE PASSING ON TO THE NEXT.

MAKE IT A RULE . . . WHENEVER POSSIBLE TO HOLD THE FILLING CAN OVER THE TABLE, SO AS TO PREVENT ANY T.N.T. DRIPPING ONTO THE FLOOR.

Just a final word . . . . . before you do the pouring or breaking down, make certain that the filling socket is in position to protect the threads of the shell.

Freddie THE PERFECT FILLER!

paramount to the good heath of those employed.[21] Pamphlets issued by the Home Office endorsed and expanded the conditions stated in the Factories Act. One of these[22] stipulated that clean overalls were an absolute essential, as was the cleanliness of the workplace. To encourage new employees to quickly become familiar with this safe working system a bonus payment was instituted. It was also suggested that process workers should keep their eye an others who may have recently started work, to make sure that they were working properly and safely.

Many of the new starters began work in the empty component stores where they unloaded the empty shells and cartridges, placing them in their respective storage bays. All the production shops had to be kept supplied with empty components to fill with explosive compositions. During 1941 a system was evolved in which the stores would supply components to the filling and assembly shops at certain intervals. This meant loading trucks ready to be collected by the electric dillys and taken to the filling shops. This was done over a 24 hour system of three shifts. The main components to be included in this schedule were shells, bombs, fuzes, cartridge cases, and primers. A rota was worked

67

Posters

The use of posters in the factory canteens and workplaces was prevalent in the war years. They were used as propaganda to encourage more work, better attendance and competitive rivalry with other explosive groups. In addition there were those referring to wartime economy measures, such as saving coal and electricity, avoiding breakages to cups and windows, and the returning of bottles.

Inter-group competitiveness was introduced to try to increase productivity and was encouraged by the group incentive bonus. The posters showed graphs with comparisons of production output between groups, the words of encouragement on the poster asking 'CAN WE DO BETTER?'

The safety/correct assembly posters included several cartoon characters. One of the most famous of the characters used on the posters of the safety department, which were used throughout all the ROFs in the country, was 'Calamity Claude'. He was featured doing all the wrong things, constantly a liability to himself and those around him; tripping, letting things fall, stacking boxes incorrectly, loading wagons incorrectly and so on, all of which stated 'DON'T YOU BE A CALAMITY CLAUDE!'.

A variety of characters were used to demonstrate the correct ways of working. 'Dickie Det' was formed with a detonator for a head and body, having arms and legs. This character was shown in the correct places within the many sub-assemblies which made up the whole round of ammunition, with captions stating 'THIS IS WHERE I FIT'. There was also a 'Mr Cap' who was depicted in a similar way.

The workers who were involved with the hand filling operations on shells, bombs and the like, had their own character. This was 'Freddy the Perfect Filler'. Freddy was shown alongside work instructions as to how stores were to be filled correctly with explosive compositions. He even showed the importance of marking shells and their boxes correctly, with statements on the poster saying 'MAKE SURE THE GUNNER CAN READ YOUR STENCILLING EASILY'.

Other posters showed soldiers at their posts and in aircraft dropping bombs, with the caption 'THEY CAN ONLY BE AT THEIR POSTS IF YOU HELP THEM BY TURNING IN REGULARLY'.

Some posters were purely informative, such as those for War Savings which, it was claimed, were 'ONE IN THE EYE FOR HITLER'. Some told of how much ammunition had been sent out to the allies fighting at the front, always of course asking for greater effort. One actually stated that 140,000 cups were issued in the factory in 1944.

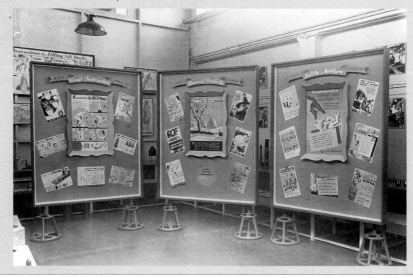

out for the collection of truck loads from the store as follows: starting on the afternoon shift at 3.15 p.m., then every 20 minutes until break-time from 5.55 p.m. to 6.25 p.m., Recommencing at 6.35 p.m., then every 20 minutes until the last at 9.35 p.m. This was a total of 18 truck loads per shift from only one storehouse.

The Process Research Department was tasked with the job of improving production methods and/or increasing the rate of production where possible. The continuing work of this department was a necessary one, for many of the tasks which were being done during storage, handling, and assembly or filling operations, were started up hurriedly, without a great deal of planning. A section of a report produced in June 1941 [23] described the work done by the Process Research Department since the factory had been completed and full production began. It noted that the methods for the filling and assembly of the following stores had been improved: 25lb shell/cartridge assembly; 2lb shell and packing; Anti-Tank mine filling; 2" Trench mortar assembly; pour filling of shells generally; 4.5" Anti-Aircraft shell assembly; 4.5" Howitzer shell assembly; Bofor shell assembly; receipt/storage of empty shells; and various improvements to the layouts of the filling shops. A further report from 1942 also noted that the factory Development Department, which looked at the introduction of new stores and the layout of production shops along similar lines to Process Research, had been 'trouble shooting' in respect of problems with the external suppliers which were 'outside the factory control'.[24]

Chorley's contribution to the war effort

Not only was Chorley the largest of the Royal Ordnance filling factories during the Second World War in terms of physical size, but it also employed over ten percent of the total work force of Royal Ordnance (20% of the 150,000 employed in filling munitions), and along with the other sixteen filling factories (including Glascoed and Swynnerton) was responsible for the munitions output for Britain's war effort, at least in the European theatre of operations.[25] It was a key element in ensuring that Britain's army, navy and air force had munitions of the right quality and quantity during the fight with Germany. Ultimately the contribution of the men and women at ROF Chorley to the war effort was so great as to be virtually incalculable.

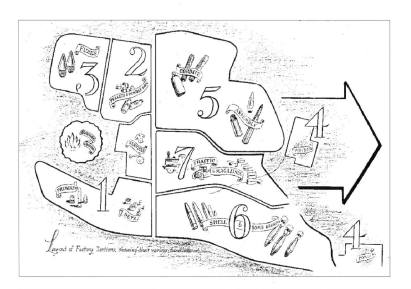

Layout of Factory Sections, showing their various functions

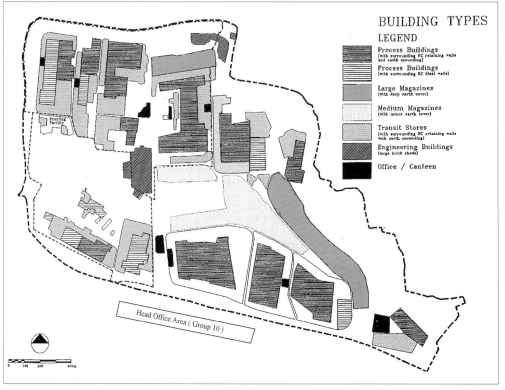

CHAPTER FOUR

Aftermath: Chorley, 1945–1957

Reorganisation and rationalisation

Although Britain was economically exhausted at the end of the Second World War, with foreign debts of £3.25 billion and economic dislocation because of the need to mobilise the whole economy for war work, the new Labour government was determined to maintain a world role commensurate with Britain's position as one of the pre-war great powers. This meant both rebuilding the economy and maintaining a credible armed service capable of working across the globe.[1]

A key factor in the re-organisation of the armed services was the role of the extensive network of state run and privately owned ordnance factories. As late as 1946 there were over one million people still working in the production and distribution of munitions. In contrast to the view expressed by the McKinnon Wood Committee in 1919, which suggested that the civilian industry could bear the brunt of any extra wartime production, in 1945 the Committee on Alternative Work for the ROFs noted that 'wartime experience had demonstrated beyond question that the best war potential was in the ROFs'.[2] Also in 1945 Sir George W. Turner, second secretary to the Minister of Supply, noted that: 'A government decision has been given that ROFs are to be maintained in peace on a scale much greater than after the 1914–18 war ... the rapid decline in orders for the fighting services makes it urgently necessary that alternative work be placed with the factories ... It was the government's firm intention to use the ROFs to the maximum ... their retention as war potential could only be effective with a keen, live labour force keyed up to the job ... It was a deliberate government policy that the ROFs should be used for any civilian production of which they were capable – not as a last resort but actively and immediately, in satisfaction of the desperate shortages in a large range of civilian needs. It was intended to allocate orders to the ROFs on production policy grounds which would override considerations of cost, but within reason.'[3]

Thus, the government took the view that it needed to maintain a state owned and run armaments industry which could be ready for rapid conversion and expansion in the event of war. Government expenditure on defence had tripled during the war and as a percentage of GNP had risen to over 20%, but this fell sharply immediately after the war to 6.5% by 1950. Compared to the pre-war average of 3%, however, expenditure remained high throughout the 1950s, 1960s and 1970s, at around 5% of GNP, with peaks at times of crisis and with Great Britain's increasing commitments to NATO.[4] In peace time it was envisaged that the

Plate 4.1 (ref 4.20). In Group 5 shells were fitted to their cartridge cases. The empty brass cases had to be cleaned before use, and the buildings used for this were 507 and 508. The cases were hung from an undulating conveyor and were dipped into tanks containing caustic soda, hot water, sulphuric acid, cold water, and hot water, in that order.

Plate 4.2 (ref 4.19). After the cartridge cases had been cleaned by dipping, they were removed from the conveyor and transported to small machines like lathes, where the cases were manually polished using sand and sawdust. To complete the cleaning process, the cases were placed on a conveyor, and passed through a heated tunnel, after which they were issued for use.

role of the defence industries was to undertake specialised tasks, and to teach other industries its techniques in mass production, organisation and distribution, and to play a pivotal role in mobilisation in the event of war.[5]

Consequently, between 1946 and 1948, there was a rationalisation of production. The reduction of filled ammunition produced by the filling factories in 1945 dropped from 2,500 tons in April 1945 to 133 tons in December 1945 and to 17 tons in July 1946. At ROF Chorley, for instance, the only filling work that was being done in late 1945 and early 1946 was on 6lb shells.[6] As production was reduced so was the workforce. The total number employed at the ROFs dropping from a peak of around 350,000 to nearly 50,000, with around 5,000 employed at Chorley. This represented a reduction in ROF sites from 44 in 1945 to 21 in 1950 (including the headquarters at Woolwich Arsenal in addition to four other factories which were held in reserve) in four groups, although this figure rose to 23 factories in 1957 after re-armament had begun.[7] The Filling Group comprised just three sites in 1950: Chorley, Glascoed and Swynnerton, with a further two in reserve (Burghfield and Thorp Arch) which were re-activated in 1952–53. The Explosive Group had four factories left:

73

Bishopton, Bridgwater, Irvine and Pembrey. There were six factories in the Ammunition Group (Birtley, Blackburn, Maltby, Patricroft, Radway Green and Wigan), and seven factories in the Gun, Carriage and Tank Group (Cardiff, Dalmuir, Enfield, Fazakerley, Leeds, Nottingham and Poole).[8] In 1949 there were also changes in the way the ROFs were administered. The Ministry of Supply, which had overseen the ROFs, was merged with the Ministry of Aircraft Production to form a new ministry employing 13,369 civil servants on non-defence work and 20,053 on defence work.

In order to be ready for rapid conversion to war time production and to maintain employment levels, a policy of undertaking civil work was introduced at the ROFs as part of the 1946–8 re-organisation.[9] Furthermore, the government was committed to ensuring that there was a high and stable employment level and the experience of previous conflicts suggested that immediate

Plate 4.3 (ref 4.35). The photograph shows 3.7 inch cases being fitted with number 9 primer. The primer is being screwed into the base of the cartridge case.

Plate 4.4 (ref 4.36). Once the shell is fitted to the cartridge case, it only remains for the fuze to be fitted to complete the 'full round'. This photograph shows the fuze, type 208, being screwed to the nose of the round. The base of the cartridge case, fitted with primer, is protected from damage on the bench, by a wooden board. The small 'air gun' is used to clean screw threads and holes in the fuze prior to fitting.

closure should be avoided. Consequently ROFs took part in the Alternative Work Programme set up by the Labour government.

At Chorley this post-war civilian work took the form of several major products; pre-fabricated houses, concrete railway sleepers, Preservation, Identification and Packing (PIP), and clothing, all manufactured using the group system, with the job broken down into a series of simple processes. Along with Glascoed and Bridgwater, Chorley produced a type of pre-fabricated building.[10] However, the main military work in this immediate post-war period was the breakdown of surplus ammunition (see below).

The Berlin Airlift in 1948 and the Korean War (1950–1953), in which Britain and her allies took part, demonstrated the continued need for British armed forces and a British armaments industry.[11] Consequently, a programme of re-armament began in 1950.[12] Re-tooling in 1950–51 indicated that engineering practices and management in the ROFs had slipped since the end of the war. Thus, in September 1952 the government installed a Board of Management for the ROFs which included industrial directors.[13] The Korean conflict led to an increase in the requirements for ammunition, which was maintained from the mid-1950s by

Plate 4.5 (ref 4.32). More 'fuzing' of shells is shown in this photograph. The shells are for the 4.5 inch Howitzer gun. They are being packed into boxes holding two only. To the left, on the truck, the shells are still fitted with their temporary plugs, prior to fitting the fuze.

Plate 4.6 (ref 4.37). Fuzes of many types were filled and assembled at Chorley. The photograph shows a production line for fuzes. Note the different 'operation stage' notices, above the production line or 'track'. The operative is watching the operation of fuze 'shutter springs' being spun at 4,500 to 6,500 rpms, which simulates the spin of a shell when in flight.

a renewed emphasis on foreign arms sales, which were used to offset the cost of new weapons systems, to arm allies and to influence potential allies.

A Royal Ordnance directive of 1 September 1950 required the alteration of some group numbers at Chorley to standardise group numbering with group function throughout Royal Ordnance. Thus Group 7 (the magazines) became Group 11D, and Group 6 (bomb and shell filling) became Group 8. At the same time these three factories were integrated into one filling group.

The consequences for ROF Chorley of the re-armament engendered by the Korean War was the stopping of the alternative work and the re-deployment of the existing workforce on filling work. Thus, Chorley, along with Glascoed and Swynnerton, returned to its primary role as a filling factory.

Along with this re-organisation came new products and processes. By 1957 Chorley had begun to mechanise some of the production of detonators, fuzes, primers and shells, and was filling larger rocket and GW motors, as well as engine starters and similar cartridges for the Royal Air Force.

Post-war work at Chorley: ammunition break down

In many of the theatres of war huge stockpiles of ammunition were surplus to requirements. Much of this ammunition had been 'in the field', in boxes that had been roughly handled and stored in the open. The wetting of the box contents caused corrosion of components and in many cases rendered them un-safe. So much so, that some dumps of ammunition could not be removed from their location, and had to be blown up where they stood.

Ammunition which was considered to be less dangerous was sent back to the ROF filling factories. Here the ammunition was to be 'broken down' and where possible the metals and the compositions in them recovered. Where the ammunition was considered too dangerous to be 'broken down', following an inspection of the box contents by inspectors at the factories, it was to be destroyed by explosion, or 'blasting' as it was termed.

The majority of the ammunition returned to ROF Chorley was of small calibre, much of it being 20mm and 40mm cannon rounds. Larger calibre ammunition tended to be returned in a

Opposite: Plate 4.8 (ref 4.1). A view in one of the explosive group canteens at Chorley during the mid 1940s. Behind the employees sitting at tables is a stage, where concerts etc. took place. The noticeboard on the stage states, 'Menu', which shows that on this day (it was a Friday) fish and chips were on the day's menu. The canteen may well have been on Group 1.

Plate 4.7 (ref B119/18). Fuzes, like all munitions, need to be watertight. Sealing of joints and screw holes in the fuze is achieved by using a composition called 'luting'. Here we see a fuze being sealed between the dome and the body. The fuze is fitted into a holder and turned by hand to apply the sealant.

Plate 4.9 (ref B18/19). It was not just shells and bombs which were filled by hand, using the steam jacketed 'kettles'. Here we see much smaller items being filled. These are 'Type 69' grenades, which are arranged in recesses on the bench. Attached to the top of the grenade are filling 'headers', which ensure the item being filled is 'overfull' to compensate for the shrinkage of the explosives as they cool.

Plate 4.10 (ref 4.33). Taken in February 1946, in filling shop '6B8' (later 8B8), this general view shows the fuzing and packing of Mortar Bombs. These are received from the right and are moved to the left, along the benches, being unplugged, sealed, and fuzed, prior to packing in wooden boxes.

Plate 4.11 (ref 4.34). In this view, we see a close up of the fuzing operation as carried out on the mortar bombs, seen in the previous plate. The bomb is held firmly in a bench 'jig', which holds the tail fins whilst sealing and tightening of the fuze is carried out.

Plate 4.12 (ref 4.7). One of the post-war jobs undertaken by ROF Chorley was the manufacture of clothing. This varied from services uniforms to industrial clothing. The work was done in building 10C30, a former stores building, close to the administration building. This was referred to as the 'Clothing Factory'. Here we see a part of the sewing shop. The building was converted into the RO Ammunition Division Headquarters in the late 1980s.

better condition than smaller calibres. The reason for this was that the bigger shells were packed in their own containers, with one or two shells per container, which were sealed against the environment. As these containers were much heavier they were handled less.

The process of breakdown comprised the separation of the shell from the cartridge, removal of the cordite charge from the cartridge, then the firing of the primer at the base of the cartridge. The fuze was removed from the nose of the shell where fitted, and any tracers/explosive in the shell removed. A final inspection of the recovered metals was carried out before a magnetic test was done to separate steel cartridges from brass, after which they were bagged for return to the manufacturer. A similar system for the breakdown of the medium and large calibre shells was carried out, for despite their size their make up and contents were the same as the small calibre rounds, except for the quantity.[14]

There were several ways in which the ammunition could be disposed of apart from the 'breaking down' operation. These were by boiling out, by sea dumping, by burning or furnacing, or by explosion. The latter task was delegated to ROF Chorley, which had to develop a suitable technique as part of the continuing breakdown and reduction policy.

The returned ammunition came into ROF Chorley by rail, and was shunted to the northern end of the factory to a large open area on Group 5 adjoining the perimeter fence running along Dawson Lane (the Dawson Dump). The boxes of ammunition were unloaded and stacked in their respective type, each of the stacks being separated by sandbag walls, the whole stack being covered by a tarpaulin. A second dump, also in Group 5, was established in 1947 at the northern end of Central Road and was therefore known as the 'Central Road Dump'.

The poor condition and sensitivity of much of the returned ammunition led to the introduction of special safety rules for the handling, movement and stacking of the ammunition boxes by personnel working at all the dumps in the factory. The risks were considerable for the boxes could explode either during examination or during transportation.

Trial work on the destruction of returned ammunition

Plate 4.13 (ref 4.5). The 'Clothing Factory' or sewing shop had a large number of female employees, who did much of the cutting, sewing and pressing work. This view, taken on Christmas Eve 1947, shows the women in festive mood.

commenced in early 1947. From the outset many problems were encountered, especially meeting the safety distance requirements in place for the explosive filling and assembly shops a short distance away.[15] The requirement for ROF Chorley to develop a system for the destruction of unsafe ammunition meant that these safety regulations still had to be observed. The greatest area of danger was closest to the factory, and was called the red zone; beyond this was a pink zone which was less likely to have damage occur to it if a major explosion should take place. The site where blasting took place posed another set of health and safety problems. It had to be done away from the production shops, and away from the ammunition dump itself. Yet some of the ammunition was too dangerous to move any distance; therefore, a special new blast cubicle had to be designed and built.

Whilst this work was being undertaken more ammunition was coming into the factory. Small dumps were established alongside the railway tracks, where possible, en route from the marshalling sidings to the northern side of the factory. Inspection cubicles, made from sandbags with tarpaulin roofs, were set up so that the boxes of ammunition could be sorted into their respective categories, as 'safe to breakdown' or for disposal by other means.

The inherent dangers of ammunition breakdown were highlighted in 1948 when an accidental explosion occurred during the opening of some returned ammunition boxes, although fortunately this happened in a contained area which prevented a more serious incident. At the time of the accident, when the hazards were perhaps at their greatest, approximately 200,000 boxes of ammunition whose condition was unknown were held in the factory.[16] The situation as revealed when the boxes were examined was often frightening.[17] The fuzes fitted to many of the shells were the most sensitive part of the assembled ammunition round. These were very often so corroded that it would have been impossible to unscrew them from the nose of the round.

Despite the urgent need to dispose of the most corroded of the ammunition, as late as the start of 1948 the blasting cubicle was still being tested. After fifty trial blasts in the new cubicle the walls were riddled with cracks, even though they were made of reinforced concrete two feet six inches thick. This problem was not solved until steel strapping was fastened around the outside of the walls, the roof removed and baffle plates fitted instead, which allowed the pressure to be released more easily, thus lessening the forces on the side walls.

In the meantime, the only way that the most dangerous ammunition could be got rid of was by 'boiling out'. Boiling out cubicles were built using sandbags for the walls. In these buildings large steam heated tanks of boiling water were used to immerse/apply steam jets which expanded the shell together with their joints, allowing the water or steam to get inside and thus remove the explosives.

With the problems resolved, seven more blast cubicles were built during 1948 and 1949. In addition, during 1950 and 1951, 30 more inspection cubicles were built in an attempt to increase the rate of disposal. Extra boiling out units were built which were better designed and equipped than the originals. These units, called cells, comprised a series of radially arranged temporary buildings for opening the boxes, with the main boiling plant in the centre. One hundred men were employed at the factory ammunition dumps and disposal areas. On top of which were 16 supervision staff. This may seem like a high figure, but due to the hazardous nature of the work supervision needed to be more intense than in the rest of the factory.[18]

Until the breakdown of ammunition by disposal methods could be speeded up, the total number of boxes in storage remained static. Calculations based on the figure of 200,000 boxes held suggested that with all the disposal facilities working flat out some 2,000 to 3,000 boxes could be disposed of at the factory weekly. During 1951–52, with all the blasting cubicles working, 6,000 blasts took place. In March 1952 it was estimated that another 40,000 would be needed to clear the dumps and it was anticipated that by early 1953 the Dawson Dump would be fully cleared, 100,000 boxes having already been disposed here between April 1951 and March 1952.[19]

The great variety of ammunition types broken down or destroyed at ROF Chorley does not appear to have survived the years. Oral evidence[20] suggests that very large numbers of 4.5″ AA shells, 4″ naval shells and 6lb shells, and Trench Mortar Bombs of differing calibres were all broken down at the factory. As regards the small calibre rounds retained in the main Dawson

Plate 4.14 (ref 4.22). Another post-war job that was undertaken at ROF Chorley, was that of 'PIP' or 'Preservation, Identification, and Packing'. This work covered the sealing, marking and packing of many items, from small to large. These items were sent to areas which were in need of all types of equipment etc., following war damage or shortages.

Plate 4.15 (ref 4.23). PIP also covered sealing and waterproofing the items being packed in containers. Here we see diesel generators being sealed. After this operation, the generator was wrapped in metal foil, which can be seen on the floor ready to be applied to the generator. The foil was then covered with a 'greaseproof' paper, sealed with adhesive tape, and the completed item packed in wooden containers.

The Engineering Department

The Engineering Department was responsible for the maintenance of the factory, and covered all work of a civil, mechanical and electrical engineering nature. It was also responsible for doing all minor new schemes and new plant layouts as production demanded. The department manufactured all the tools that the factory required and, in addition to maintenance of mechanical plant, manufactured special purpose plant items urgently needed by other Ministry of Supply establishments and ROFs.

During the 1940s and 1950s the factory had five boiler houses, three of which had turbo generators and, in addition to the factory's consumption, often supplied excess power to the National Grid through the North Western Electricity Board. The main engineering workshop consisted of workshops as follows: General Machine, Structural, Tool Room, Instrument, Electrical, Pipe, Woodworking, Vehicle Repair, Engineering Development, Wagon Repair, Crane and Lifting Tackle. There was a small workshop on each of the production groups, a special workshop for Process Research, and one for work classified as top secret.

In the mid to late 1950s the total strength of this section was 70 staff and 900 industrials, both skilled and semi-skilled, the department spending around £800,000

each year on maintenance. In addition to this, each year in the 1950s there was around £50,000 worth of capital work on prototype and other plant manufacture for other factories and establishments. The department also controlled Chorley's fire brigade, which had its own engines.

and Central Road dumps, here too there was quite a variety. The only details that have survived concerning the types of ammunition held relate to 1952.[21]

Post-war work: manufacture of concrete houses

ROF Chorley, and two other Royal Ordnance Factories, undertook the manufacture of house components made out of concrete. These were produced from moulds into which wet concrete was poured, vibrated and allowed to set.[22] These prefabricated houses were the invention of the notable architect Sir Edwin Airey of Leeds, and were referred to as Airey houses. The houses were built from the concrete components except for the roof, which was of traditional wooden design. Production of the houses at ROF Chorley, started in 1946, and continued until around 1950 or 1951.[23] These structures were two storeys high and constructed from slabs of reinforced concrete set horizontally and vertically, each slab overlapping the one below. At ROF Chorley the daily rate of production was enough panels to build five houses, whilst the storage area for panels held enough for 60 houses.

The building where the wall slabs and wall posts were produced was a former storehouse known as 11 DB 2, situated off the Central Road. This building had a rail connection at one side, and a loading bay for wagons at the other. The cement, sand and aggregate used in the mixing of the concrete was all kept within the building, to ensure they were kept dry and that the correct mixture proportions were used at all times.

Houses manufactured at ROF Chorley were delivered to sites all over the north, whilst those manufactured at the other two ROF's supplied the south of the country. Many of the houses were built locally around the Chorley district. The nearest to the factory were in Euxton Village, less than a mile away. These were built close to conventional brick houses in which some of the staff from the factory were housed.[24] The houses purchased by the local authorities were delivered to their building site by the factory vehicles having trailers. Due to the weight of the concrete panels it took five trailers to carry a pair of houses. Houses for transportation to more distant locations were loaded onto rail wagons at a purpose built loading platform adjoining the storage area. Once all the components of the Airey house had been delivered to the building site, and a concrete raft for the foundations prepared, it took two weeks to build a pair of houses. The internal fittings were undertaken by Ministry of Health appointed companies.[25]

Like the Prefab, the Airey house was not intended to be a long term home. They were built quickly to deal with housing problems. They did not have a great aesthetic appeal but they were functional. Some of the houses are still in use today, although few of them survive as originally constructed, most having had their concrete walls replaced by brick. This was due to the corrosion of the metal rods passing through the posts, causing movement of the walls.[26] In the village of Hoole, six miles west of ROF Chorley, three pairs of Aireys are still unaltered, one pair of these being of the early pebble-dashed type.[27]

Post-war work: manufacture of concrete railway sleepers

Sir Charles McLaren, Director General of Ordnance Factories (DGOF), released the news that the manufacture of Concrete Railway Sleepers was to begin at the factory whilst addressing journalists on their first visit to ROF Chorley, in July 1947. Work had begun in April within a large former storehouse numbered 11 DB 1, which was located to the east side of Central Road. Road access was via an existing loading bay on the south, and the factory railway system passed the building on the west side. The building was of steel frame construction, with corrugated iron walls and roof. It was level throughout, except for the loading bays and access ramps, which made conversion of the building straightforward.[28] Excavation work inside the building began in May 1947 at the north and south ends, which had to be extended.[29]

By December 1947 the concrete mixers had been installed, plus the wire spool and tensioning trucks. Some of the production lines with their ancillary equipment were completed, and the first sand and stone aggregate arrived at the new plant. The first working trials took place soon after on two of the production lines, with half of the lines (22 out of the total 44) nearing completion. In January 1948 the two lines were producing 72 sleepers a day.[30] By June 1948 22 lines were producing 1440

sleepers each week, and this rose to 2,500 a week when all the lines were completed.

Though the new plant in building 11 DB 1 was not yet fully operational, management were looking to increase production. A number of buildings were considered for conversion, including 507 and 508. The problem with these buildings, however, was that at the time they were being used for cartridge case cleaning, a process which, it was anticipated, would be needed again, although in 1948, as the production of ammunition was at a low, the plant was not in use. It was decided, therefore, to relocate the plant. It was envisaged that if the plant was needed again, it would not need to be on the same scale so could fit into a smaller building.

The need to create a floor space of at least 540 feet × 150 feet for the installation of a second sleeper production plant was much easier to accommodate in the 508 complex, though some extension would be necessary to accommodate the concrete mixing platform and the aggregate bins. Though the second plant was

Plate 4.16 (ref 4.50). The late 1940s saw British Railways desperately short of wooden sleepers, due to importation problems. Accordingly, ROF Chorley set up a plant to make them from concrete in a storehouse on Central Road during 1947–48. There were 44 tracks producing the sleepers, and this view shows them being produced on 16 tracks only (to the right), the other tracks being as yet incomplete.

Plate 4.17 (ref 4.5). As the concrete sleepers were moved down the track, gradually curing, they were vibrated and trowelled level at their base (uppermost in the moulds). This operation is under way in the photograph. Note the reinforcing wires passing through the mould ends.

Plate 4.18 (ref B352/131). The completed sleepers were demoulded, as shown here, and inspected for cracks, faults etc. There was no storage or stacking yard for the sleepers, which were sent out as quickly as possible after the approved cure time. Rail wagons ran into a loading bay inside the building. This building (11DB1) later became a storehouse again.

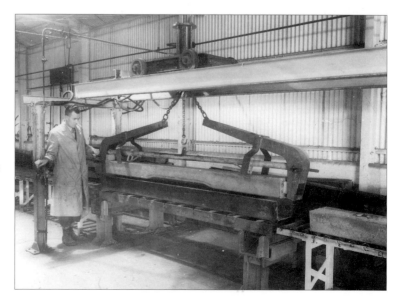

intended to have 44 production lines, it was found that it could accommodate more, and 52 lines were installed. The lengths of the lines in both plants were the same, and could accommodate 36 sleepers lying end to end on each line. Work on the second plant started in February 1948, and pilot production began in mid October. The anticipated production from both of the plants was 250,000 to 300,000 sleepers per year. Production at ROF Chorley continued until 1952 and accounted for 25% of British Railways' total requirement of 1,000,000 new sleepers per year.[31]

Post-war work: clothing manufacture, PIP, and tools

Another post-war job which had gained momentum since the end of the war was the manufacture of clothing. A tailors shop had existed throughout the war, its main purpose being to make and repair all items of clothing that were used in the factory.

The tailors shop, or the 'Clothing Factory' as it was known after the war, was located near the administration building on

Plate 4.19 (ref 4.2). Yet another concrete product was made at ROF Chorley in the post-war years, starting in 1946. This was to make parts for 'Airey Houses', which were of the 'prefabricated type'. Chorley produced panels and posts which, when fastened together using metal rods, made up into a house. Here we see the stock yard for these components, which were produced in the building later numbered '11DB2'.

Plate 4.20 (ref 4.3). This view shows one of the factory 'scammel' tractors, with trailer loaded with house components for local delivery. Many of these houses were built locally, in Euxton, Charnock Richard, Leyland, Hoole etc. The components were despatched from the factory by rail, and by private road vehicles to locations all over the North West.

the southern side of the site. It was enlarged during 1946 and 1947 and extra staff were taken on.[32] New lines of sewing machines were installed, along with additional cutting tables and presses, and larger store, finishing, and pattern rooms were built.[33]

The production of clothing by the Tailors Shop was not the sole output from the building. Textiles were also used for making packing material, washers, spacers, discs, cambric strips for priming, exploder bags, and cordite charge bags.

A separate section within the shop – called the component shop – produced corrugated packing, paper sheets and other bits and pieces which were used for the manufacture and assembly of packaging materials for the ammunition produced at ROF Chorley.

The post-war production of ammunition boxes at Chorley was a development of work which had been done in war time. Countless thousands of these boxes had been made in ROF Chorley's box shop during the war. These had been made not only for packaging ammunition made at Chorley, but were sent to other RO factories for their use. Although the volume of ammunition production had been greatly reduced at ROF Chorley following

the end of the war, there was still limited production work in progress and new ammunition boxes were still needed.[34]

The expertise gained during the production of boxes at ROF Chorley was to be further developed. This new work was be called Preservation, Identification and Packing, or PIP. Where the infrastructure of towns and cities had been destroyed or badly damaged by air raids, there was a desperate need for products such as diesel generators, water pumps, electric motors and small items which needed to be protected from the environment. These included items such as electrical and radio equipment, engines of all types (for use in wagons and cars), military equipment, machine parts and gears, radar antennae, as well as many other small items all of which had to be correctly packed for despatch overseas.

The first part of the operation was to preserve the item. How this was done depended on the component itself. It might be dipped in grease, wrapped in grease paper then packed. An engine, on the other hand, had to have all its openings sealed before being wrapped in tinfoil. Packages or crates had to be large and strong enough to carry the contents in a sealed environment.

Plate 4.21 (ref 4.21). In 1948 this display of post-war work was set up in the 'clothing factory'. It shows, from left to right, concrete sleepers, in and out of their moulds, plus a very futuristic steam locomotive illustration. In the centre can be seen the clothing produced at the factory, behind scrap metals recovered from breakdown of ammunition. To the right are Airey House components and 'jigs and tools' made for private industry.

These heavy cases had to be built in one of the buildings which had rail access. The diesel generator sets, for example, weighed over a ton and were between twelve and fifteen feet long by six feet high and wide. During the first half of 1946 seven hundred people were employed on this work at ROF Chorley. Two production lines were dedicated to dealing with motor vehicle parts from nuts and bolts to engines for the forces of the United Nations and the Netherlands government.[35]

The work on PIP at Chorley continued until the production of munitions on a large scale re-started in 1951,[36] when the shops in which the crates had been assembled were once more used for the storage of empty shells.[37]

Re-armament at ROF Chorley, 1950–1957

The decision to re-arm in 1950 was felt at ROF Chorley in the following year.[38] By the end of March 1952 ammunition filling had increased by 87%, whilst alternative work had been reduced by 47% compared to the year ending March 1950. The workforce had also been increased at Chorley from 3,742 in April 1951 to 4,675 by the end of March 1952.[39] Re-activation also led to extensive modernisation and refurbishment of the factory. Nearly £500,000 was spent on the factory in the period 1950 to 1952, half of it on the following:

Installation of 24,000 ton presses	£130,000
Installation of press and tube cutting machinery	£1,650
New assembly & filling unit and machines	£10,000
Improved rail access to factory sidings etc.	£5,000
Improved layout, cordite cutting	£5,000
Improved layout ball rotor filling	£5,000
Improved layout 2" rocket motor filling	£5,000
Development work etc., pyrotechnic stores	£5,000
Filling plant, FSDS improved layout	£5,000
Tooling and formers for new ammunition	£15,000
New 1,000 KV x-ray unit	£15,600
Restoration of sleeper unit building, 508	£22,150

In addition there were changes to the fuze, tracer and rocket assembly filling shops, plus other smaller alterations, including the provision of more toilet blocks, improvements to shop layouts, and door widening.[40] The result of this investment was an expansion of production. Between 1950–51 and 1951–52 total factory expenses rose from £1,613,000 to £1,879,000 and the production of shells and cartridges rose from 408,000 units to 537,000 units, whilst the number of fuzes made rose from 1,648,000 to 3,329,000, and primers from 895,000 to 1,292,000.

As production increased two shift working was re-introduced. Most of the work done by Chorley in the period 1950–57 was for NATO contracts; approximately one third of the workforce was deployed on this work and 85% of the shells filled during 1954–55 were for NATO use. Chorley also filled sub-assemblies for all the other factories doing NATO work, including ROF Pembrey.[41]

The re-activation of ROF Chorley as a filling factory led to

Plate 4.22 (ref 4.14). At the end of the war, there were vast amounts of ammunition in 'dumps' throughout all the former 'theatres of war'. Much of this had been in 'front line' situations, often in adverse conditions. Many ammunition boxes were damaged, allowing the elements to start corroding the contents, making them unsafe. This was the condition that the ammunition was in when received at ROF Chorley, as the photograph shows.

Plate 4.23 (ref 4.16). The returned ammunition came into ROF Chorley by rail. It was then shunted to the 'dumps' on the factory. Once unloaded, it had to be inspected, to determine if it was unsafe, and be destroyed. If it was safe it was broken down in the shops. The inspection cubicles were made from sandbags, with a lightweight roof of tarpaulin as shown above.

other changes. During the war there had been major advances in electronics and related disciplines. In the immediate post-war period private companies were unable or unwilling to move into this area. Consequently, it was the government which promoted research and development on new products, such as guided weapons like the Blue Jay and Stooge missiles, air to ground missiles such as the Blue Boar, the surface-to-surface long range Red Rapier and the air to air Red Dean. This was done in partnership with private companies such as Armstrong-Whitworth, Fairey, Ferranti and Vickers. As part of the 1950 decision to re-arm and the re-organisation of the ROFs, it was decided to undertake high explosive research (HER) at ROF Chorley.[42]

Furthermore, in 1951 a process research department was established at ROF Chorley to undertake long-term development of the mechanisation of the filling processes and to improve efficiency, safety and the final quality of the product.[43] In conjunction with the plant and machine design section, Process Research helped design and develop special purpose machines for the High Explosive Research programme. These included machines for 'pressing', turning, boring, facing, band saws and milling machines. It also produced machines for precision casting and maturing of explosive charges. These machines were not only produced for Chorley, but also supplied to Aldermarston and Burghfield.[44]

The first step in this mechanisation process was the speeding up of the moving stream of work flowing through the process shops. This was partly achieved by using and adapting existing machinery from the food packaging industry, and by merging small shops into larger process buildings more suited to this conveyor belt approach. This new emphasis on the mechanisation of the filling process culminated in 1954–56 in the design and production of machines for a fully automated shell filling plant in Sydney, Australia, which included conveyors, filling machines, hot probing and cavity boring machines.[45]

A major addition to ROF Chorley's renewed filling and research

Plate 4.24 (ref 4.15). Following inspection of the returned ammunition, the boxes were placed in stacks, awaiting either transfer to the shops for breaking down, or destruction by blasting or 'boiling out'. The boxes were carried to the stacks by men wearing special harnesses, to avoid dropping them.

Plate 4.25 (ref B419/1). At ROF Chorley, there were two main returned ammunition dumps, plus many smaller ones. The two main ones were located on Group 5; one to the north east, called 'Dawson Dump', the other on the west side of the group, and called 'Central Road Dump'. This view shows part of the latter dump, which later became much bigger than this view shows.

roles came in 1955 when it was decided that Project 'M', and related Projects 'Q' and 'S', should be undertaken at Chorley.[46] These were part of the atomic weapons programme and ROF Chorley was involved in the manufacture of components and sub-assemblies for the bomb. £3.2 million was allocated to Chorley for this project, and an assistant director responsible to the DOF (F) (Director of Filling (Factories)) was appointed to look after the project, which included the design of special electronic weighing and stemming machines, plastic moulds and filling equipment. Though staff assigned to this project were experienced RO personnel, all of whom had signed the Official Secrets Act, they were again vetted. The sensitive nature of the project meant that even when parts of the manufacture were sub-contracted, vetted Chorley staff were posted at the private company to oversee the work.[47] This work was concentrated on Group 508.[48] Although the scope of the project was reduced in 1956, limited test production continued until 1960–61 and research until 1981.[49]

Factory life

The biggest change in the factory life of ROF Chorley during this

period came with the reduction of the workforce. At the end of the war in 1945 the total workforce within all ROFs was approximately 350,000,[50] with perhaps as many as 30,000 still employed at ROF Chorley. Within six months of the end of the war, this workforce was reduced. Some of the excess workforce was deployed in the re-opening of peace-time factories closed for the duration of the conflict. In Lancashire a huge number of cotton mills had closed and their workers had moved into the munitions industry. Gradually the cotton mills began to re-open and the women who had been 'in cotton' returned to their respective mills. Some of the stresses caused by these changes were captured by the local press in mid 1947. One article was headed 'Chorley MP Told Ex Servicemen Losing Jobs To Women'.[51] The report alleged that married women were replacing ex-servicemen at ROF Chorley, whilst the local cotton mills were 'crying out' for women operatives. In reply the Ministry of Supply in an article entitled 'Women Not Systematically Replacing Men',[52] stated that ex-servicemen were being discharged in accordance with union agreements and it was the choice of the women to work at ROF Chorley instead of in the cotton mills.[53]

Apprenticeships under the Ministry of Supply were still available at the ROFs and the many research and development establishments around the country. A few craft apprenticeships

Plate 4.26 (ref 4.10). In addition to the breakdown of small calibre ammunition such as 20 and 30mm, large shells were returned to Chorley to be broken down. These were usually still in their original packaging and undamaged, which allowed them to be broken down without undue risk. This view shows the separation of shell from cartridge case.

Plate 4.27 (ref 4.27). During the early 1950s ROF Chorley produced much filled ammunition for NATO. This work was largely the filling of shells, particularly 90mm. The layout of the shop production line for these shells is seen here during the early 1950s.

had been extant during the war years at ROF Chorley and this figure had slightly increased by 1952. Even so, there were fewer than 20 apprenticeships. Wages for 16 year olds started at 29 shillings a week, rising to 66 shillings at the age of 20, with a possibility that 'in ten years time they could be earning perhaps £3,000 a year as senior engineers or scientists'. At ROF Chorley, apprentices had a system whereby they worked in all the sections of the factory for periods of time, plus working in the apprentice training centre 8½ hours a day, four days a week, with one day off for education.[54] By 1957, rates of pay for apprentices had risen slightly; at age 15 years they got 43 shillings and 11 pence, rising to 141 shillings and fourpence at age 21. Apprenticeships were being offered at 22 ROFs, 15 research establishments and three inspectorates. The types of apprenticeships available were Craft Apprenticeship, Drawing Office Apprenticeship, Student Apprenticeship, Electronic Apprenticeship, and Pre-University Graduate Apprenticeship.[55]

The reduction in the size of the workforce meant the closure of the three hostels. Washington Hall, which had never been used as a hostel although it had been occupied by the USAAF between 1942 and 1945, was taken over by the Lancashire Education Committee in 1947 and became an emergency teacher training college for women. Later in the 1960s the Lancashire County Fire Service took over the hall as one of their training centres.[56] Woodlands Hostel closed in January 1955, by which time there were just 200 residents, rather than the 2,000 it was built for.[57] Highways Hostel was the last to close. In 1952, when it still had over 700 residents, it had been taken over by the Ministry of Supply from the joint YWCA/YMCA committee which had run it in the immediate post-war years. A proposal to close the hostel in 1959 because it was losing money led to staff forming a company to run it as Highways (Euxton) Limited. In this form the hostel continued, with over 300 residents, until its final closure in September 1963.[58]

Despite the reduction in the size of the workforce the social

Plate 4.28 (ref 5.24). During the early to mid 1950s, 'palletisation' was the only way to handle goods, including empty components coming into ROF Chorley. Many trials were carried out, including some using rail wagons being 'rough shunted' during the trials. With road transport delivering more and more new pallets, equipment, such as fork lift trucks and side loaders (as shown here) was required.

life of the factory continued, particularly the sports activities. The sports field on Alker Lane eventually became the official playing field for the factory team which played in the local Chorley and District Alliance League and in the Royal Ordnance Factories Sports Association League (ROFSA). The first inter-factory sports event took place in late 1947, when ROF Chorley competed against ROF Maltby. In the evening the visitors were entertained to a concert performed by members from many of the factory's musical and entertainment groups.[59]

Other social activities in the factory included gardening clubs, amateur dramatics, a choral society, an angling club, a swimming group and other clubs which were unofficially organised by representatives on each group or section of the factory.[60]

Arising from this plethora of sporting and other activities a committee was formed to look into the possibility of making a purpose built factory sports club, where all the sporting and other recreational groups could get togther, and where home games could be played and bowling greens set up. Tennis courts were erected on a site close to the stores building 10 C 30, at the south east corner of the factory. The land adjoining the tennis courts was large enough to create football pitches, but was in need of levelling and drainage work. Work began on the site for the new sports and social club during mid 1947 and much of the work was done on a voluntary basis by factory personnel.[61]

Change and continuity

Over the period 1945 to 1957, ammunition filling had ceased and restarted, civilian work had come and gone, the high number of the workforce had been reduced then slightly increased. Remaining as a part of that workforce were personnel who had gained expertise and experience during the war years. A changed and more versatile culture had emerged, its evolution continuing during the 1950s as more technical requirements were emerging. The ammunition being produced was of a more technical nature, a trend which was neatly summarised in a 1956 pamphlet, which noted that:

The impetus given by war time necessity has continued to a

large extent since 1945, particularly in the Royal Ordnance Factories which act as repositories for large scale production techniques. The process research now going on at the ROFs, and in particular, the interest maintained in work study ensure that, should the need for sudden expansion again arise, Britain will be in a far better position to meet it than she was in 1939.[62]

CHAPTER FIVE

From Royal Ordnance Factory to Plc, 1957–1984

Government defence policy, 1957–1979

In April 1957, following the 1956 Suez Crisis, a Defence White Paper was published which was officially described as 'the biggest change in defence policy ever made in normal times'. The main thrust of the White Paper was that 'Britain's influence in the world depends first and foremost on the health of her internal economy and the success of her export trade. Without these, military power cannot in the long run be supported. It is therefore in the interests of defence that the claims of military expenditure should be considered in conjunction with the need to maintain the country's financial and economic strength'.[1] What this meant in reality was a return to the long-standing policy of relying on high-technology solutions which allowed workers to stay in factories, helping Britain to maintain its industrial might. Consequently, the Royal Navy and the Royal Air Force were to be reduced in size, conscription abolished and there was a shift towards the development of high-tech weaponry.

For the ROFs this review led to the greatest changes since the end of the war. The government continued to recognise the importance of the ROFs as 'a major industrial concern comparable in size with some of the largest engineering and industrial organisations in the country'. In a policy statement issued by the Ministry of Supply, also in April 1957, the aims of the ROFs were laid down as follows: 'to provide a source of production for all Controllers; to be a preferred source for general stores (munitions) as before; to extend their operations into the new modern weaponry planned; to act as a source of engineering for

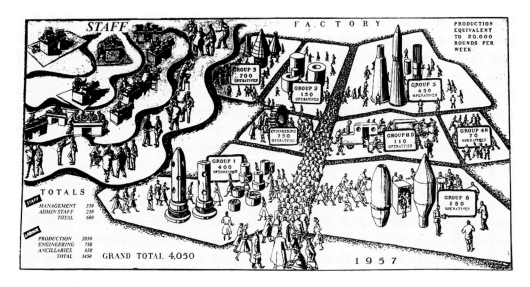

production and the manufacture of experimental equipment to the requirements of the Research and Development establishments; their capacity was to be kept 'fully efficient and up to date'; and to be allowed to undertake civil work when there was 'a shortage of suitable capacity in industry, or where it is necessary to retain special expertise for defence purposes'.[2] The factories were to be maintained with sufficient emergency reserve capacity so that production could be doubled during times of war. Thus in 1954 and 1955 the various divisions of Royal Ordnance were working at an average of 43% and 44% capacity, an average that was maintained throughout the 1960s and 1970s.

The review reduced the number of ROFs from 23 fully operational sites in 1957 to 14 by 1960, with a consequent drop in the workforce from 47,600 on 1 March 1956 to 30,050 by 1 March 1960. Those factories that were closed between 1957 and 1960 were Cardiff, Dalmuir, Fazakerley, Irvine, Maltby, Poole, Swynnerton, Thorp Arch and Wigan. The remaining factories (Birtley, Bishopton, Blackburn, Bridgwater, Chorley, Enfield, Featherstone, Glascoed, Leeds, Nottingham, Patricroft, Pembrey, Radway Green and Woolwich, plus one in reserve – Ranskill) and their combined workforce of 30,000, were to be organised into four groupings according to the type of products (Weapon and Fighting Vehicles Group, Ammunition Group, Filling Group and Explosives Group). Each group was under a group director with

Plate 5.1 (ref pallets). By 1955, when this photograph was taken, the use of pallets was the normal way to receive incoming components. This was applicable to both rail vans and road vehicles. Here we see cartridge cases on pallets being unloaded from an ROF Birtley trailer in building 508.

direct responsibility to the Controller of the Royal Ordnance Factories (CROF) In addition there were three directorates covering the whole of the ROF organisation: administrative, financial accounting, and engineering services. Finally, as part of the changes in defence policy recommended by the review, responsibility for the factories was moved from the Ministry of Supply to the War Office.[3] These changes were to set the character of Royal Ordnance for the next generation, and although changes were made to the status of the ROFs in 1973, the structure of the organisation as established in the period 1957–60 remained in place until privatisation in 1985.

When ROF Chorley was established in 1936 it was directly funded by the government through an annual parliamentary vote.[4] This meant that parliament had to approve annually the sum of money available to the Royal Ordnance to meet its operating costs for the next financial year. In 1968 the then government appointed Sir John Malabar to examine the ROF's organisation and accountability with a view to removing some

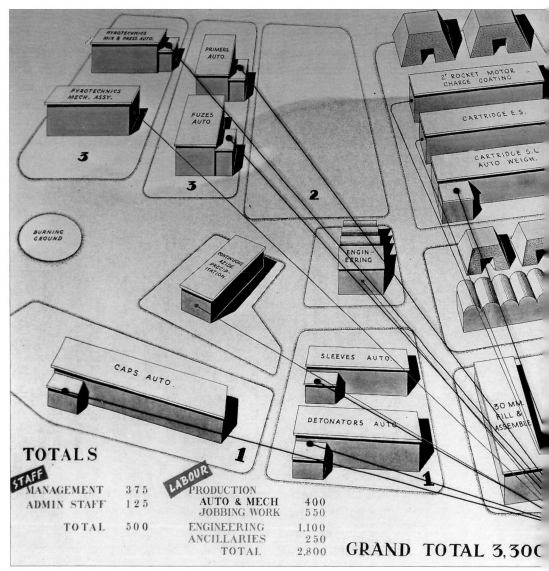

Plate 5.2 (ref 5.25) 3 of 3. At Chorley during 1956/57 attention was focused on the 'Strategic Plan for ROF Chorley'. This contained proposals for the rationalisation of ROF Chorley, through modernisation and automation rather than job losses The diagram shown here illustrates what was being considered for the factory layout at that time, and the workforce required.

of the main constraints which inhibited the commercial potential. The role of the ROFs was at this date reactive rather than innovative. Unlike manufacturers in the private sector, the

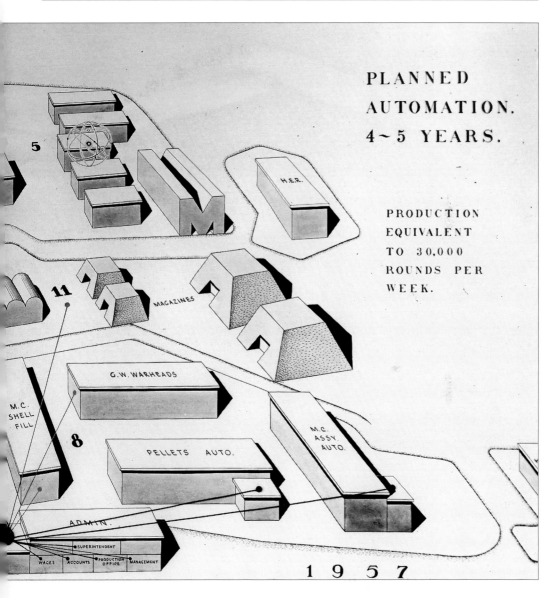

PLANNED
AUTOMATION.
4~5 YEARS.

PRODUCTION
EQUIVALENT
TO 30,000
ROUNDS PER
WEEK.

1 9 5 7

organisation was not free to design and develop products which
in its judgement would find a profitable market. It had to organise
and equip itself to respond to the demands for products which
were designed elsewhere.

The finding of the Malabar Committee was that the ROFs
should be commercially viable and resulted in the setting up of
the ROF Trading Fund within the Procurement Executive. In
July 1974 funding and control moved to the Trading Fund, so

Plate 5.3 (ref 5.1). The 1950s saw the introduction of an employees' children's outing, which became an annual event. In this view, taken on the 'Flat Iron' market place in Chorley in about 1956, the children pose by their buses. The centre bus is a Leyland 'Royal Tiger', a very popular 'new' bus of the time. The outings were very often to Blackpool Tower Circus.

that the ROFs, though owned by the government and administered by the Ministry of Defence, operated in a similar fashion to a private company. Each of the eleven main ROFs and the two Ministry of Defence subsidiaries (employing a total of 23,000

people) was now a commercial enterprise able to accept contracts from private firms.[5]

In the late 1950s and early 1960s total turnover for the ROFs had been around £30-£35 million.[6] By 1974/75 sales had only risen to £81 million, which allowing for inflation was not a great increase. Furthermore, the proportion of sales overseas remained virtually static; in 1959/60 it was 16.6% of turnover whilst in 1974/75 it was 17.4%.[7] The new Trading Fund was instrumental in allowing sales to rise from £81m in 1974/75 to £263m in

111

Plate 5.4 (ref 5.29) or B 515/2. During the early and mid 1950s, ROF Chorley was producing large quantities of 3.5 inch HEAT rockets. This photograph shows the operation of 'indenting', or 'stabbing', to secure fuze to tail, and fuze to head. The 'head' end, to the left, contains the explosive charge.

1977/78.[8] Profits in this period amounted to £122m for taxpayers and £516m earned in exports during the period 1973–8. Consequently, the ROFs won the Queen's Award for Export Achievement in 1976 and 1978, whilst employment in the factories actually increased in this period.[9]

The early 1980s proved leaner times for the ROFs, with the loss of overseas orders (particularly with the collapse of the

Plate 5.5 (ref 5.9). Inspection of filling and assembly work on explosive stores during the war years, was done by a process known as 'Patrol Inspection'. This was still used in later years, but changed slightly to include a 'monitoring' system. The 'monitors', wearing white overalls in the photograph, move from shop to shop, recording their findings as they visit. Notice the epaulettes worn by the monitors.

Iranian arms market after the Islamic Revolution in 1979),[10] increased overseas competition and cuts in the British Army's requirements affecting sales in 1981 and 1982. Royal Ordnance had a turnover in 1979-80 of £283 million, which dropped to £278 million in 1979–78 and was £281 million in 1980–81.[11] In the period 1978–82 the workforce dropped from around 23,000 to 19,400 through natural wastage and some redundancies.[12] However, the ROFs attempted, with some success, to expand their overseas market by breaking into the USA military market and into Egypt, where assistance was given with the building of a new munitions manufacturing plant.[13] This enabled the ROFs to turn in sales of £350 million in 1981–82, £449 million for the year 1982–83, and a turnover of £481.9 million (and a profit of £55.9 million) for the year 1983–84 (Chorley contributing significantly to this total),[14] and to win the Queen's Award for Export Achievement in 1983.[15]

113

The move towards privatisation

The election of a Conservative government in 1979 led to a change in the position of the remaining 11 ROFs and, ultimately, their privatisation as part of the government's plan to reduce the public ownership of industry. This represented a major shift in government thinking and was, in effect, a return to the policy pursued by successive governments during the 1920s and early 1930s, and to the private provision of munitions that was the norm before the eighteenth century.

The first step towards the selling of the ROFs came with the government's defence review initiated in 1981. This led to a commitment to increase defence expenditure in real terms by 3% per annum. The main determinants of defence policy remained the threat from the Soviet Union and her Warsaw Pact allies, and Britain's commitments to the NATO alliance. In 1982 Britain spent more on defence than any other major European ally, both *per capita* and as a proportion of gross domestic product. ROF Chorley was directly affected by these increases as it was required to help re-equip the army, especially through the deployment of the Challenger main battle tank (manufactured

Plate 5.6 (ref 5.14). The re-armament work arising during the early 1950s, saw many orders being produced at ROF Chorley for NATO. One of the orders was for the production of 90mm shells, which occupied many shops on the factory. Here we see the 90mm shell/cartridge assembly shop on Group 5.

Plate 5.7 (ref 5.15). A closer view of the cartridge/shell assembly machines used on Group 5 during the 90mm NATO shell contracts. The machines were operated by compressed air.

at ROF Leeds), and the introduction of a new 120mm high pressure gun capable of firing the new armour piercing anti-tank ammunition. New requirements for the RAF also had an impact through the purchase of the Tornado GR1 with its Mauser cannon produced by ROF Enfield and filled by ROF Chorley, and the Tornado F2 with its Sky Flash air-to-air missiles.[16]

The impact of this review was far reaching but for the ROFs proved one of the most significant turning points in their history, marking the retreat of the government from its policy of state munitions production and the principals of the Hacking committee of 1934 which had been re-emphasised by the Mallabar report of 1968. On 20 May 1982 the Defence Minister John Nott announced that 'the ROFs should no longer operate under the Government Trading Fund Act, 1973, but in a more commercial environment under the Companies Acts ... Initially thereafter Government ownership will continue but with the intention in due course of involving private capital directly – either through sale to the private sector, joint venture, or flotation of shares. Meanwhile, in line with the recommendations of the 1981 study group report, relevant MOD design and development capabilities

and sales functions will be transferred to ROF control as soon as possible'.[17]

The Trading Fund arrangements for the ROFs was not a true reflection of what it was to be a private company. As Geoffrey Pattie, Minister for Defence Procurement, noted in 1983 'the ROFs' present operations under the Trading Fund prevent them from realising their full potential'.[18] Therefore, as part of the progress towards privatisation the ROFs were re-organised in advance of the creation of four subsidiary companies.[19] The Ordnance Factories and Military Services Act of 1984 allowed the Secretary of State for Defence to transfer ROF assets to one or more private companies. These companies were to be: RO Ammunition Division, which would contain Birtley, Blackburn, Chorley, Glascoed, Patricroft and the agency factory at Featherstone; RO Explosives Ltd which would contain Bishopton, Bridgwater, PERME (Propellants, Explosives and Rocket Motor establishment) Westcott, PERME Waltham Abbey and the agency factory at Summerfield; RO Small Arms Ltd which would com-

Plate 5.8 (ref 5.18). The 'tightness' of the crimped joint of shell to cartridge case was of paramount importance. This joint had to withstand the gas pressure build up of the propellant charge in the case, up to a specified pressure. To ensure the 'tightness' was correct, a 'Pull Off' test was carried out at regular intervals. This plate shows a 'pull test' rig, with a shell in place. The shell base is annotated as follows: 'Amm Lot ROF 1–8, Shell M71'.

Plate 5.9 (ref F 244). Completed ammunition was stored in underground magazines, which were of two types; one having a single open room, the others, as above, had several long, narrow chambers. The magazine type for storage was dependant on the amount of explosive contained in the ammunition itself.

prise Enfield, Radway Green and the agency factory at Powfoot; and RO Weapons and Fighting Vehicles Ltd would cover Leeds and Nottingham.[20]

Implicit in the move towards privatisation was a rationalisation of the work undertaken by the ROFs. A major change in attitudes would be needed to compete effectively in a commercial market.[21] The ROFs enjoyed exclusive manufacturing rights to certain types of armaments and relied on other Ministry of Defence departments to supply most of their marketing efforts overseas. Thus, in 1983/84 only 36% of Royal Ordnance's turnover was exported, the rest going to the British government as their preferred supplier, a market which the new company might not be able to rely upon.[22]

Consequently, the role of many ROFs, with their large percentage of mothballed buildings (amounting to as much as 50% in a number of cases) was now in doubt. Trade Unions within the ROFs, including Chorley, started to campaign against privatisation arguing that the Mallabar Report had rejected such a sale

117

Steam and electricity generation at ROF Chorley

ROF Chorley was powered by both steam and electricity, generated on site by five boiler houses originally built in the period 1937–39. The steam produced was of both low and high pressure. Low pressure (10lbs to 50lbs per square inch) accounted for over 50% of the total steam used on the factory and was used for the heating of workshops, power for the explosive filling shops and processes, and the canteens and offices. Process heating, direct and indirect, was confined mostly to Group 8, and canteen cooking equipment. For this use, steam was required at 10lbs to 50lbs per square inch, and where necessary, the steam was reduced further in pressure by the use of reducing valves.

Steam was required at 60lbs per square inch for process work and heating Group 4 South, and a small boiler house was set up here, independent of the main boiler supplies of steam. This was known as Number Five Boiler House. The factory low pressure steam main supplied this group with heating steam at 15lbs to 20lbs per square inch only. Laundry presses and hot air driers, installed in the Laundry and the Clothing Factory, needed steam at 60 to 80lbs per square inch. This was provided by two stationary oil fired locomotives, adjoining the building. During a typical week, in the winter months, the boiler houses raised over 12,000,000lbs of steam, and burned over 1,000 tons of coal.

Five boiler houses produced electricity for the site, numbers 1, 2 and 3 being located on the north east side of the factory. This location ensured that the smoke and grit was carried away from the factory by the prevailing winds. Each of these three boiler houses had a turbo generator adjoining, having a 2,750KW capacity. A feature of these three boiler and power houses was that they were interconnected by a high pressure steam main, enabling any of the three power stations to operate from any boiler house. This was in addition to the low pressure steam main interconnection.

The three boiler houses had 8 Lancashire Boilers, arranged in two banks of four. Each of the

Lancashire Boilers were 30 feet long by 9 foot 3 inches in diameter and had a working pressure of 250lbs per square inch. They produced steam to drive Daniel Adams turbines and English Electric turbo generators rated at 2,750kw with switchgear by Brookhirst. Electricity generated at ROF Chorley was primarily for use on the factory, but was also exported into the National Grid and vice versa.

There were two other boiler houses within the site. Number Four Boiler House was located on Group 1. It was equipped with four John Thompson 'Super Economic' Boilers, which gave a total output of 48,000lbs of steam per hour, with a working pressure of 120lbs per square inch.

Number Five Boiler House was installed on Group 4S to supplement the mains steam supply, which, due to the distance travelled, had a pressure drop. The process work on this group needed steam at a higher pressure than the main supply. The small boiler house consisted of 2 Clayton and 1 Farrer vertical cross tube boilers. This boiler house was closed in the 1960s.

In 1971–72, Numbers 1, 2 and 3 coal-fired boiler houses were closed and a new oil-fired boiler house built between numbers 1 and 2 boilers, now closed. This new plant generated all the electricity required by the factory. It was closed in the mid-1990s. By 1998, only the former Number Four Boiler House remained in use, supplying Group 1.

and that the 19,000 workers in the ROFs would lose access to the skills and expertise in the rest of the civil service.[23] Nevertheless, as part of the move towards privatisation and improved efficiency, the re-orientation of the ROFs towards the market place began, and as part of these initial steps the first small-scale redundancies were announced in November 1984, affecting the factories at Birtley, Bishopton, Blackburn and Chorley.[24]

Chorley and reorganisation 1957 to 1960

The 1957 Defence Review had a severe impact on the ROFs since the demand for their products was to be much reduced. This required the closure of many of the ROFs which were now surplus to capacity. Within the Filling Group, ROF Chorley was seen as a key site since the factory was 'capable of filling all types of gun ammunition and bombs, but at the present time, not pyrotechnics or ammunition below 40mm calibre. It is a premier filling factory, employing more people than the others, having the best facilities, and being the nucleus for the greatest number of staff with their technical knowledge. It was intended, and built, to be a permanent factory, and can draw labour from all directions, the labour being good.'[25] The fate of the other filling factories was not so secure.

Whilst Chorley was to be kept, two of the remaining filling factories were to close. The first to go was Swynnerton, a

Plate 5.10 (ref 5.22). The explosive filling within a shell body had to be without cavities, for these could cause premature detonation of the shell. To ensure that the filling was without cavities, or any other 'foreign bodies', the shells were all x-rayed. This view shows a 1,000 K.V. x-ray unit, which was used to check shell production.

Plate 5.11 (ref 5.19). Filled sub-assemblies also had to be x-rayed, to ensure no foreign bodies were present! This was particularly important on fuze assembly. The fuzes were x-rayed on trays, and the developed film checked for any faults by 'readers' who worked in darkened rooms searching for faults, as shown here.

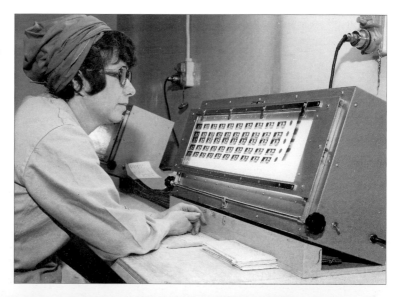

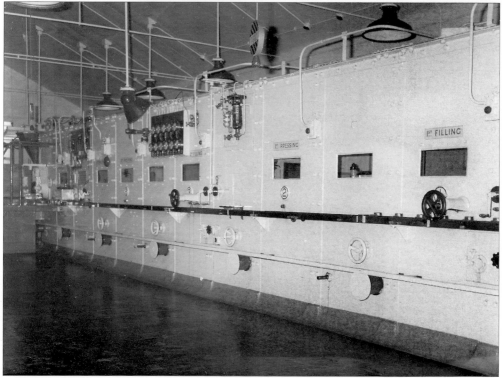

Plate 5.12 (ref 5.21). Taken in 1968, and little changed today 30 years on, the above view shows an auto detonator filling plant, on Group 1 at ROF Chorley. They were usually referred to as 'fortresses', for they were built like these! The empty detonator cups were fed in at one end, and filled during their 'flow' through the 'fort'.

121

temporary factory, which was closed in June 1958 since it was the most expensive of the factories to run. Shortly afterwards it was decided to close Thorp Arch as well and to transfer Burghfield work to other ROFs. The decision to close Thorp Arch rested on the value of its assets compared to those of Glascoed; the latter had assets to the value of £4,855,420, whereas Thorp Arch had assets valued at £4,176,785. Thorp Arch was closed in December 1958. In addition to the closure of these two filling factories, the

Plate 5.13 (ref 5.20). Reference has been made to the shell pressing chambers nicknamed 'Queen Marys'. Here, shells are being pushed into one of the chambers. Once inside the chamber, the shells would be positioned under a press used to consolidate the explosive filling of the shell. This photograph was taken in building 8J39 in February 1968.

Plate 5.14 (ref 5.12). Hand filling of shells had gradually been replaced by auto filling during the late 1950s. By the 1960s shell filling at Chorley was being done on a conveyor system. Here we see part of a shell filling line in building 8J40, the shells about to progress into the 'Queen Mary' pressing chamber.

four reserve filling factories at Brackla, Elstow, Risley and Ruddington were also closed in this period.[26]

Nine ROFs were shut in the period 1957–60 due to the Defence Review. Consequently, a large amount of work was transferred to the remaining factories, including ROF Chorley. In September 1957 this new work at Chorley included 30mm cap production and igniter N8 production. In the same year extra fuze capacity was transferred from ROF Swynnerton, as was plant and equipment for 30mm High Explosive (HE) assembly. In 1958 the latest production techniques for 2″ and 3″ rockets were transferred from Thorp Arch, along with further fuze production and some cap filling for the 9mm and 303 caps.

The cost of this reorganisation was high, amounting at ROF Chorley to over £1.5 million. This was because it involved the remodelling of many buildings on most of the groups to accommodate the transferred work. The group by group costs were: Group One Initiator Composition Section £65,000; Group 1 east,

Plate 5.15 (ref 5.6). The 1960s saw ROF Chorley being used for things other than ammunition production! One of these activities was civil defence training. The centre for this was at Old Worden Hall, where a complex of 'demolished' buildings was used to create accident and emergency simulations. Training of local police, firemen, civil defence groups and army personnel, was carried out, with local volunteers being used as 'victims'.

Plate 5.16 (ref 5.5). A rescue simulation is shown here circa 1968, at the Old Worden Hall training site. Taking part in this exercise are army personnel from the R.A.M.C., all ranks, from corporal to captain. The rubble and timber simulating demolished buildings was 'made up' to create any scenario, for rescue purposes.

detonator production £169,000; Group 1 west, cap production £140,000; Group 3 east, fuze filling £167,000; Group 3 west, pyrotechnics £286,000; Group 8 east, miscellaneous ammunition £265,000; Group 8 central, medium calibre shells £145,000; and on Group 8 west, 30mm HE and practice £212,000.[27]

ROF Chorley 1960–84

At the end of the Second World War there were 17 filling factories employing around 150,000 people, all undertaking work by hand. By 1957 this figure had dropped to around 12,000 people in five filling factories (Burghfield, Chorley, Glascoed, Swynnerton and Thorp Arch). As a result of the 1957 Defence Review and subsequent re-organisation the workforce of the filling factories dropped to 6,001 in the year 1959/60 and declined further to 5,319 in the year 1960/61, based in two factories, Chorley and Glascoed.[28] Throughout this period ROF Chorley continued in

125

its role as a filling factory, with a workforce of 'semi-skilled labour, much of it female'. Despite the transfer of extra work, and the refurbishment of many buildings, by March 1961 large parts of the 928 acre site had been mothballed and the workforce had been reduced to 3,442.[29] Further advances in mechanisation and the introduction of computerisation (which was considered as early as 1957)[30] during the 1960s meant that by March 1972 the workforce had been reduced to 2,027 comprising 1,465 industrial personnel and 562 non-industrial staff, although women workers continued to form a significant proportion of the staff at 31.6% (or 642) of the total.[31] Retention of the 14 ROFs, though many were largely mothballed, was part of the government's stated policy of readiness; in theory factories such as ROF Chorley could be brought back into production within a few weeks, since excess production capacity was over 50% of the maximum output of the factory.

Although much of the site was mothballed, and expense on

Plate 5.17 (ref 5.8). Local fire brigades also trained on the reservoir at ROF Chorley, where rescue/training exercises were carried out. Here the use of an inflatable boat with water pump on it is the task in hand. This involvement with fire training was a precursor to the setting up of a fire training centre at the former factory hostel, Washington Hall.

Plate 5.18 (ref Fire Engine). ROF Chorley Fire Brigade had, until the later 1980s, two fire engines. One of these was a 1970 machine, the other, shown here, was of mid 1980s' vintage. These were sold and replaced by a double rear axle Range Rover and a small emergency van. The view above shows the 1980s RO Chorley Fire Engine, with some of the Fire Department personnel.

Plate 5.19 (ref 5.61). Retirements, especially of long serving personnel, used to have a special significance. Their period of work within the ROF organisation was highlighted on a scroll, composed by John Stanley, the factory Chief Illustrator. Here we see Factory Director Mr Purcell (centre), presenting scrolls to Messrs Wills and Hughes in 1974.

the buildings was kept to a minimum,[32] the group system remained intact. Thus Group 1 continued to manufacture initiating compositions and to fill detonators and caps. Group 2 pressed the exploder pellets for fuze magazines, booster and supplementary charges. Group 3 undertook much of the additional capacity transferred to Chorley in the years 1957 and 1958, and this involved the refurbishment of some small shops which were joined together to make large process buildings more suited to the new mechanised filling process. Group 3E undertook the filling of fuzes for shells, whilst Group 3W filled pyrotechnic

Plate 5.21 (ref 5.4). The factory Transport Department was always a busy one, for it maintained a large number of varied types of vehicle, including buses. Seen here are some of the buses and the personnel who worked on them. Taken during the mid 1970s (about 1974). The plate shows Director Mr Purcell, in centre, at a retirement presentation.

Plate 5.23 (ref 5.64). All the factory groups had their first aiders, who were part of the factory first team, and who took part in inter factory competitions. These were held at different locations within the ROF organisation. This plate shows the ROF Chorley team in 1976, winners of the St John Ambulance Challenge Shield.

Plate 5.24 (ref 5.7). The Royal Navy has had a toehold at ROF Chorley since the factory's completion in 1940. The FQCD (Factory Quality Control Department) Proof Yard was where normal production samples were sent to be fired. This ensured that all stores produced were made as per specification. The Naval Proof Yard did additional work for Naval contracts, but also did 'factory proof' on certain stores.

stores and time fuzes. Group 5 prepared and assembled cartridges and filled primers and Group 8 filled high explosive shells.[33]

The re-organisation of the ROFs set the pattern of the organisation until privatisation, although there were a number of changes at ROF Chorley in the departments and products during this period. In October 1962 the Ammunition and Filling Groups were merged into one with a total workforce of 11,984, of which 3,114 were based at ROF Chorley in March 1963.[34] By amalgamating these two groups it was anticipated that delays in the supply of empty components to the filling factories could be eliminated and thus costs reduced. Other attempts to increase efficiency in the early 1960s included the adaptation of Chorley's filling processes. Thus in November 1962, the under capacity small calibre filling section was adapted for the filling of medium calibre shells, for which capacity on the site was tight.[35] Attempts at tighter quality control continued throughout this period. Until the 1970s the Quality Control of ammunition production was based on MoD (Procurement) 'Inspectorate of Armaments' (I Arm) procedures, and the 'Technical Requirements' (TRs) raised by them. The TRs covered all the different aspects of production quality control, in association with other 'standards', such as Defence Standard DEF–131-A and Defence Guide 7 (DG 7). In 1969, the Raby Report recommended that new policies and proceedures for the inspection of MoD products should be set up.

This was further endorsed by the Rayner Report, and these recommendations were incorporated into the 'NATO, Allied Quality Assurance Publications'. A draft of this new standard was accepted by the MoD Procurement Executive (PE) in 1972 as the 'Defence Standard 05–21' series.[36] ROF Chorley achieved approved 05–21 status in 1977, and this in its turn was replaced by new NATO requirements known as the Allied Quality Assurance Publications (AQAPs) in 1984.[37]

A number of new departments were established at Chorley in this period including the ROF Centre for Management Studies (CMS). This unit had originally been set up in 1949 at ROF Swynnerton. In 1956 it had moved to the Royal Arsenal at Woolwich and in 1967 it moved to Chorley and was housed in a purpose built centre which included air conditioned lecture rooms, a CCTV area, common room, and library. CMS was responsible for the centralised training of all ROF staff in the management and supervisory aspects of their work, and organised courses on other subjects applicable to ROF needs. In 1971 the newly formed ROF Computer Bureau, responsible to the Director of Ordnance Factories (Accounts), was established at ROF

Plate 5.25 (ref 5.67). The factory Training Centre, in building 8A3, was where many internal courses were held. One of these, the NEBSS (National Examination Board of Supervisory Studies) course, was compulsory. This plate shows attendees from this course having received their certificates. To the right of the photograph is Mr John Stanley, who was at this time (1976) Chief Training Officer.

Plate 5.26 (ref 5.66). Before privatisation, the factory was kept 'secure' by the Ministry of Defence Police, who patrolled the site and manned the gates. Some of the police were trained 'dog handlers'. The dogs which are shown here with their handlers, were kennelled at South West Stores.

Chorley, to deal with the computerisation of the payroll, bill paying, accounting and statistics.[38]

The establishment of the Trading Fund allowed greater investment in plant and machinery and divided the ammunition and filling sides of the business. During the period 1974–84 Chorley witnessed the biggest building programme since its construction.[39] There were also further significant developments in the mechanisation of the filling process.

One of the biggest programmes of the 1970s, requiring new equipment and a new building, was LAW 80 *(continued on p. 143)*

Plate 5.27 (ref 5.69). The trade union representatives on the factory often had to deal with 'unbending' senior management during negotiations. In mid 1978 a productivity agreement for the FQCD (Factory Quality Control Department) was under negotiation. This photograph shows the agreement being signed by Factory Director Mr Jim Lavin, and the union conveners, along with other shop stewards/management also present.

Plate 5.28 (ref 5.3). The Sports and Social Club of the factory still continued to play an important role in the inter-group rivalry stakes, as it had since it had been built. This photograph shows a factory team circa 1978/79.

Plate 5.29 (ref 5.70). The Good Housekeeping Cup was not just sought after by the explosive filling groups. All factory departments were in the running for the cup. In 1978, the cup was won by one of the services departments – an 'unlikely winner' it was said! This gang of men moved anything, from machinery to office furniture, around the factory. The photograph shows some of the gang and staff, with the cup, in the former Box Shop.

Plate 5.31 (ref 9–3271c). Following the prize giving ceremony, the senior guests visited the Apprentice Training School in the Services Section of the factory. In this view, the VIP guest in 1977, Sir Sydney Bacon, MD ROFs, is seen on the left, with Apprentice Supervisor Tom Horrocks, and one of the apprentices.

Plate 5.33 (ref 5.68). Photographs were taken of all attendees at CMS courses, and this picture illustrates the fact that CMS courses catered for employees from all over the country. Of the twelve men featured here, only two – Glynne Davies and Jack Smith – were from ROF Chorley.

Plate 5.34 (ref 5.17). ROF Chorley's Group 2 produced 'pellets' of explosive composition, used in sub-assemblies such as fuzes, exploders, etc. The pellets were made either as a continuous process or by filling moulds and pressing. The pellets might be 'wrapped', 'doped', 'perforated', 'shaped' etc. This photograph shows one of the continuous production presses, called a 'Manesty Press'.

Plate 5.20 (ref 5.62). A close up of a retirement scroll, typical of those produced during the mid-1980s. Buckshaw Hall was usually depicted, and on this scroll we can see the caricatured Tom Hughes in retirement. It also refers to his times at other establishments.

Plate 5.22 (ref 5.63). Awards for long service, in the form of the Imperial Service Medal, were part of a tradition, which came to an end when the company was privatised. Here we see Factory Director Mr Purcell presenting the medal in August 1974. The presentation was carried out in South Side canteen, where a buffet was laid on for the attending families of those receiving the medal.

Plate 5.30 (ref 9.3269c). The trade apprentices had an annual awards ceremony, where prizes for their achievements over the past year were presented. It was customary for the factory director to host the event, held in South Side canteen. In addition, a VIP would be there to present the awards. At the 1977 ceremony, shown above, the VIP guest was Sir Sydney Bacon, MD ROFs.

Plate 5.32 (ref 5.2). The VIP guest at the 1981 apprentice prize giving was Tom Finney, seen here with ROF Chorley's Geoff Lambert and Dave Bury.

Plate 5.36 (ref 4.2) (below). The 1950s to 1970s, saw improvements in the technique of auto machine filling at Chorley. These operations were carried out on several filling tracks, including 105mm calibre shell production, as shown here in April 1974. Four shells are positioned, ready to be filled with RDX/TNT 60/40, under the machine dispenser heads.

Plate 5.37 (ref 5.27). After filling, the shells are cooled gradually. This photograph shows 105mm shells, still with their 'jackets' and 'filling headers' in place to ensure gradual and even cooling.

Plate 5.38 (ref 5.26–1). Medium calibre ammunition included cannon rounds, such as 30/40mm calibre. Some of this was 'belted', to allow continuous fire. Cotton gloves were used by the operatives to prevent them from touching the cartridge cases which could cause marking and possible corrosion.

Plate 5.39 (ref 5.26–2). The continuous belts of ammunition were tested for correctness of spacing, and for flexibility of the belt-clips. This was done by checking sections of the belt lying on a flat table, on which a gauge, showing the 'tolerance and acceptance zones' of the belt was inlaid.

Plate 6.1 (ref 6.1843c). The plastic-bodied anti-tank Bar Mine was produced at ROF Chorley in large numbers throughout the 1970s and into the 1980s. The mines were filled on Group 8 at the factory. They were filled through their end, as shown above, whilst being clamped vertically to a track.

Plate 6.2 (ref 6.2848c). Filled shells had to be correctly marked using a silk screen. The overall paint-work of the shell was also important, ensuring that it was protected from the elements and was easily identifiable.

Plate 6.3 (ref E75). The Giant Viper mine clearing system was another ROF Chorley product. This consisted of a large diameter, 750-foot hose filled with plastic explosive. As it was filled, it was coiled into its firing trailer as shown in this photograph.

Plate 6.18 (ref 1.2175c). Inside the Boxer Cap production building, the filling process is done using a computerised track system. The track is to the left, where it is hidden behind panelling. Note the remote handling apparatus.

Plate 6.26 (ref xys). Project 'Xyster' was born out of the closure of ROF Patricroft in the late 1980s. The project was created to produce guided weapon components and sub-assemblies which had previously been done at Patricroft. Xyster work was shared between RO's Birtley, Glascoed and Chorley. At Chorley, the work was done in a modernised former services workshop, as seen here.

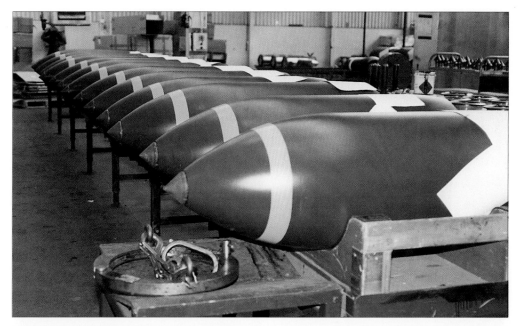

Plate 6.27 (ref GUL). RO Chorley had not seen work on 1,000 lb bombs for many years when an order for the filling of these bombs was received in the early 1990s. They were filled on Group 8, the customary location for this task. Filled bombs are seen here in the process of being marked prior to despatch.

Plate 6.28 (ref 9/9187). Completion of work on the former storehouse 10C30, into Ammunition Division Headquarters, led to the question of items for decoration/display in the building, especially within the large foyer area. This led to the acquisition, on loan, of a gun, which according to the lads from Design & Development who moved it into place, was 'heavier than they thought'!

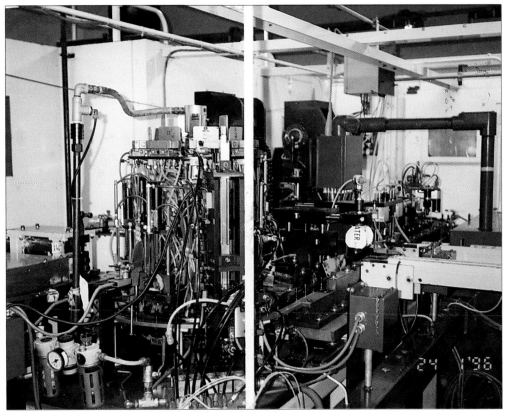

Plate 6.30 (ref IAF 005). Despite the contract for the filling of MLRS grenades coming to an end, the machinery used in the filling process was retained in case of further orders being received. Shown here is one of the grenade filling and assembly machines, with its multiple air circuits.

Plate 6.33 (ref DEM). Not all the buildings within the closed portion of ROF Chorley are concrete; many are made of brick only. Prior to their demolition it is necessary to burn them to ensure that there are no remaining explosive residues in the fabric of the building.

Plate 5.35 (ref 5.23). Group 4 North on the factory was engaged on work associated with Group 508 from the 1960s. This was officially termed 'High Explosive Research'. During the 1970s and 1980s, the group was engaged on the manufacture of plastic components for use at Aldermaston. One of the plastic component injection moulding machines is shown in this view.

(Light Anti-armour Weapon, a 'use and discard' hand held weapon which employed a collapsible launcher). This required the building of a new filling and assembly plant at ROF Chorley, which was to undertake the filling of the warheads and rocket motors and the final assembly. The motor and ignitor body came from Birtley; Bridgwater supplied the high explosive and motor propellants; the safety and firing unit were manufactured by Blackburn; the warhead and forebody components by Patricroft; the spotting rifle ammunition by Radway Green; the assembled spotting rifles from Enfield; and the launchers were built by Hunting Engineering Ltd. Production began in 1985.[40] The key element of the new purpose built complex at ROF Chorley was the automation of production, which was based upon the conveyor system which carried the products through all the various stages. Conveyor belts and chain drive were replaced with a revolving shaft lying between the rails on which the trolleys ran. Drive was picked up by a friction wheel mounted on the trolley with its axis parallel to the shaft. Gears bent this drive through 90 degrees and transferred it to the running wheels of the trolley. This new system removed the inherent dangers of continuous belts and chains which could trap clothing or fingers.

Another major product developed in the late 1970s was a new automated 155mm HE shell filling complex, which was opened in May 1979 by the Master General of Ordnance, General Sir Hugh Beach, KCB, OBE, at a cost of £1 million. The new plant which was the most modern in the western world at the time. The final design of the plant was based on extant filling procedures used at ROF Chorley. The engineering and design of the plant ensured that close control of the temperature of the filled shells was maintained. The 155mm shell with its associated cartridge case, was for use with the Field Howitzer gun. The production of the whole round required the work of several other ROFs in addition to ROF Chorley's filling work. The other parts of the round were produced at the following locations: the empty shell at ROF Birtley; ROF Bishopton which produced the propellant and combustible cartridge case; ROF Bridgwater which made the RDX/TNT filling for the shell; ROF Glascoed which assembled and packed the charge casings; and ROF Blackburn which made the fuzes which were filled at ROF Chorley.[41]

Other new facilities built during this period included buildings for the Boxer Cap production, on Group 1, and the MLRS (Multi-Launch Rocket System) programme.[42] Boxer Cap was a production facility with an automatic computer controlled track filling system that manufactured 5.56mm (Boxer) primer caps, hence the name. These were used in the assembly of 5.56mm ammunition at ROF Radway Green. ROF Chorley was responsible for filling, assembling and packing the MLRS (Multi Launch Rocket System) bomblets, various sections of which were manufactured at ROFs Birtley and Bridgwater, as well as ROF Chorley.[43]

New products manufactured in this era also included the filling of the 76mm HESH (High Explosive Squash Head) shell, which was for use against concrete fortifications, buildings and soft-skinned vehicles);[44] production of the anti-tank Bar Mine System for the army, used for the laying of minefields; and filling of the Giant Viper, which was used for breaching minefields.[45] By the late 1970s ROF Chorley was filling fuzes for radar echo

Plate 5.40 (ref 9/844). The factory railway station ROF Halt, which had seen some forty trains coming and going each day during the war years, ceased operation in the 1960s. This photograph, taken in 1965, shows a train for Chorley, with another to the left bound for Leyland. For steam locomotive enthusiasts, the loco heading the train towards Chorley is a Caprotti Black Five, numbered 44756.

and star shells for the Royal Navy, and for warheads for use in Sea Dart and Seacat anti-aircraft missiles.[46] A number of these products proved vital during the Falklands War in 1982, in particular the ammunition for the 4.5″ naval gun, the Sea Skua anti-ship missile warheads, anti-aircraft missiles and depth charges.[47]

There were also the beginnings of civilian diversification in the 1970s, for the first time since the 1950s. The Dial-a-Star was a signalling and distress flare launcher, designed, developed and produced at ROF Chorley. It was sold not only to the army but to civilians such as yachtsmen and was used during the Fastnet boat race of 1979.[48]

Factory life

The factory closures of the period 1957–60 led to a number of changes in life at ROF Chorley. The most obvious of these was a reduction in the working week from 44 to 42 hours, which took effect on 1 August 1960. Along with the drop in numbers working at the factory, there were also changes to the transport arrangements at the ROF. By 1960 the number of trains arriving and leaving ROF Halt had dropped to four each day, and in 1965 the station was closed. The factory now relied on buses to ferry the workforce to the site and in the early 1960s as many as 40 a day arrived and left; as late as 1984 there were still 32 buses each day bringing workers from all parts of central and north-eastern Lancashire (Ashton-in-Makerfield, Blackburn, Blackpool, Bolton, Darwen, Fleetwood, Hindley, Orrell, Poulton-le-Fylde, Preston and Wigan). All the outside buses would park on the Central Road car park which was marked with numbered bus lanes for each route to and from the factory. From there factory buses would ferry the workforce to and from the process buildings.[49]

In 1964 the factory celebrated its Silver Jubilee. Apart from an official photograph of the staff in front of the administrative building, and an unpublished manuscript copy of a book commemorating the event, the occasion appears to have been very low key.[50]

In 1977 and 1978 an in-house newsletter was produced at ROF Chorley, its intention being to let people throughout the factory know what was going on around the groups, socially and what products were being worked upon. It was also intended that contributions about employees' interests and hobbies should be included. The first issue included a report an a recent Gala Day held at the sports club and items on a Miss ROF dance to be held in the South Side canteen. Reports on recent retirements, weddings and other social events made the ROF Chorley Newsletter a popular read.[51]

Throughout this period the Annual Apprentice Awards at the factory were hosted by the director, senior staff and union representatives, with VIPs presenting the awards. These were usually army officers, sporting personalities, and ROF management from other factories or headquarters. The awards presentation in the South Side canteen was followed by a buffet for guests and families. The apprentices' training school was also visited by staff and the presenter of the prizes, where they were shown samples of work which had been done by the apprentices during the year.

The 1970s saw the introduction of another electrically-powered vehicle at ROF Chorley besides the dilly, this time specifically for use on the group cleanways. This was a form 'scooter' which had one small wheel at the front and two at the back, with a platform between the wheels on which the driver stood. The 'sprogs', as they were known, were allocated to those group staff who walked great distances each day carrying out their duties around the many buildings, although they were often unofficially 'borrowed'.

By 1980 very few of the original staff taken on in 1939 were still working at ROF Chorley. One of the last to retire in September of that year was Mr G. Samuel, after 43 years' service, who had been transferred to ROF Chorley from Woolwich Arsenal.[52]

Despite the retirement of most of the Second World War staff, the ROF Chorley workforce could still rise to the task during a national emergency, as the Falklands War in 1982 showed. In September of that year a letter arrived at the factory from Air Chief Marshall Sir Douglas Lowe thanking the staff working on guided weapons who had been involved in extra production of the Sea Skua missiles used by the Royal Navy Task Force in the Falklands, where the missiles had played an important role in the conflict.[53]

Continuing the tradition

The story of ROF Chorley between 1957 and 1984 was dominated by increasing efficiency and technical innovations. Inevitably, these advances led to reductions in both the number of people employed and the number of buildings in use on the site. Despite the drop in the workforce from around 3,500 in 1957 to around 2,000 in 1984, and with over 50% of the site mothballed, ROF Chorley, as one of only two remaining filling factories, was still a vital and efficient Royal Ordnance Factory.

The natural history and wildlife of ROF Chorley

During the years 1937 to 1939 between 60 and 70 per cent of the ROF Chorley site was disturbed by the construction of the filling factory. This disturbance did not only involve removing the topsoil, but also deep excavations to create magazines, the levelling of large areas on which to create production buildings, the mounding of soil around these buildings, and the diversion of streams and the creation of the reservoir. Of that original pre-1937 landscape, which was mostly farmland used for arable and pasture, only traces now remain. The 30 to 40 per cent of undisturbed land is largely woodland.

Over the factory's 60-year existence, the woodlands have been allowed to grow largely undisturbed, except for necessary maintenance of the trees and streams/reservoir which are located within the woodlands. In some of these undisturbed woodland areas, old field boundaries in the form of hawthorn hedges can still be found, with swathes of bluebells visible at certain times of the year. This rich wildlife has always been appreciated by the staff at ROF Chorley. In the early years of the factory's life there were groups of employees who got together to talk about and study it, and they even made notes on species and types. However, no detailed study of the flora and fauna was done until the running down of the factory began in 1996, at which time Royal Ordnance's Environmental Services Group commissioned an ecological assessment of the site. This survey of the site was partially based upon a 1994 survey which had included vegetation and bird and animal habitats. The 1996 survey covered birds, mammals, insects, amphibians, grass and woodlands, vegetation and plant communities, land-use and wetland areas (there are 22 ponds on the site). Two of the most important areas are the ancient Buckshaw Wood and Worden Wood, havens for a variety of bird species including kingfishers, and a small number of roe deer.

CHAPTER SIX

Privatisation and beyond

The end of government control

Royal Ordnance plc, with its four subsidiary companies, thirteen factories (Birtley, Bishopton, Blackburn, Bridgwater, Chorley, Enfield, Glascoed, Leeds, Nottingham, Patricroft, Radway Green, Waltham Abbey and Westcott), and three agency factories (Featherstone, Powfoot and Summerfield), officially came into being on 2 January 1985, vesting day as it was known, with a workforce of 20,082.[1]

The mid to late 1980s was to see some of the most radical changes in the history of the ROFs. Although Royal Ordnance plc was still wholly owned by the government, the company needed to adapt rapidly to the rigours of a competitive private sector, and to the new financial restrictions and year-by-year efficiency savings imposed by the government in its new contracts with the company,[2] if it was to have a long term future.

This new atmosphere was reflected in the relationship between Royal Ordnance and its former boss, the Ministry of Defence. Prior to privatisation the Ministry of Defence (MoD) did not hold open competitions for arms purchases, but awarded contracts to British businesses, with the emphasis on quality and reliability. The MoD supplied the specification of the product required and paid the defence contractor's development costs plus the production price. As part of the government's long term aim to reduce public expenditure through increasing competition the MoD began to open its tendering process to foreign arms contractors. From 1985 onwards defence contractors were increasingly required to pay for the research and development of a new product, without any guarantee of receiving the production contract, whilst the MoD retained the intellectual property rights.[3]

ROF Chorley Administrative Building

The Administrative Building at ROF Chorley lies on the southern side of the factory, fronting Euxton Lane. For the local community the building vies with the main gatehouse, also on Euxton Lane, as the public face of ROF Chorley.

The building was begun in 1937. Its steel-framed structure, steel-framed windows, concrete sills, and flat roof are typical of late 1930s architecture, as were the factory houses nearby. Today the building's exterior remains largely unchanged, despite its age. Inside the building, the only alterations have been to create open plan offices by removing the side walls of the central corridor. The main front entrance now has a reception desk and switchboard, instead of the old entrance foyer with its revolving door. The glass panel over the front door still has the 'KG VI 1939' inscription on it.

It is not known whether King George VI, who officially opened the factory in March 1939, went inside the building, but we know that he signed the visitors book on a table at the bottom of the main front step.

During the war years, provision was made in the basement rooms for escape in case of bomb damage, with most of the rooms being interconnected by small iron doors, many of which are still in place today. The Radio Room was also located in the basement and played an important role in war years, providing news and music from the BBC, and relaying it to the factory canteens.

Outside the building, there was once a putting green, and, so it is said, a bowling green on the lawn nearest the camera in the photograph. The building today, set in its attractive surroundings, continues to play a key administrative role within the RO organisation, under British Aerospace.

Plate 6.4 (ref 6.8). The manufacture of sensitive initiator compositions, as used in detonators and electric caps, was done adjoining Group 1, which did the filling work. The compositions were made under strictly controlled conditions, to produce crystals which were dried and blended. In the view above, lead azide composition is in the process of drying.

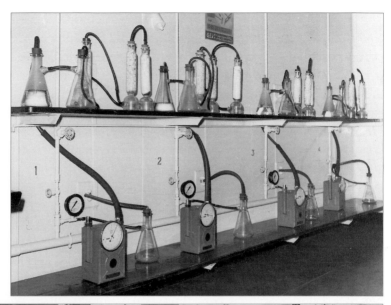

Plate 6.5 (ref 6.4). The High Explosive Research (HER) work that was done on Group 5 necessitated the use of many large presses and enclosed gas filled cabinets. In this plate a 2,500 ton press is shown, with a gas cabinet. This has glove 'arms', to allow work to be done inside the cabinet.

151

This policy of increasing competition in western Europe's largest
defence market (accounting for 25% of western European defence
expenditure) was not mirrored in neighbouring countries,
where procurement remained in the hands of defence ministries,
thus restricting the development of a free market in defence
equipment.

Royal Ordnance was particularly vulnerable to the new competitive market since it was dependent on MoD orders (in 1984
90% of its orders came from this source, which had dropped to
60% by 1990/91)[4] and products designed exclusively for the
British market. There was clearly a need to build a wider customer
base if the company was not to be over exposed to changes in
British government expenditure.

RO began entering into commercially based contracts with the
Ministry of Defence in 1985. The Ammunition Division containing ROF Chorley secured two, three year contracts; firstly to
develop and produce CHARM, a Chieftain and Challenger tank
armament improvement; and secondly to undertake the production of a new fuze for use with artillery ammunition, together

Plate 6.6 (ref 7/3065).
The internal rail
system within ROF
Chorley, was, at its
maximum, some 20
miles in length. This
total was reduced
during the 1970s and
into the 1980s, a
process which would
see the discon-
tinuation of the
factory rail system in
the late 1980s, and
access to the main
Chorley/Preston line
lifted.

Plate 6.7 (ref BM). Filled ammunition was stored in underground magazines, often referred to as 'bulk magazines', served by the factory railway system. The loading/unloading area outside the magazine was covered over and mounded for blast protection in case of an accident occurring.

with its electronic setter known as the ETF (electronic time fuze).[5] RO began paying for use of government research and development facilities. Thus, RO was allowed access to military ranges at a set cost and had to pay to use the trials range at CDE Porton Down.

The intention of floating Royal Ordnance plc on the Stock Market was abandoned in June 1986, despite making a pre-tax profit of £26 million in its first full year as a commercial organisation (on a turnover of £487 million).[6] According to the Secretary of State for Defence, Mr George Younger, speaking in the House of Commons on 17 June 1986, 'Although substantial

153

Plate 6.8 (ref 9.2342). This view looking to the south overlooks Group 5, with Group 8 in the distance, and was taken from the top of one of the magazines shown in the previous plate. The rail wagons are at the entrance to a 'transit magazine', from where completed stores for dispatch are loaded.

Plate 6.9 (ref 28/3). At the other end of the scale are small magazines, comprising a small central building, surrounded by blast protection banks. These types of magazine were the ones used on the filling and assembly group. This view, taken on Group 1 'L lines', shows a magazine used for the storage of sensitive explosive compositions.

progress has been made in the process of transforming Royal Ordnance into a fully fledged commercial entity, it has not been possible to take this far enough and to have in place all features necessary to provide the basis for a successful flotation'.[7] The government's preferred course was to sell the company to a single purchaser, although ROF Leeds, which manufactured the Challenger tank, was sold separately to Vickers plc in October 1986.[8] Full privatisation was very close, with four companies showing interest, and BAe finally securing Royal Ordnance plc with a bid of £190 million in April 1987.[9] In its last year under government supervision Royal Ordnance plc made a pre-tax profit of £29 million on turnover of £515 million, with a workforce of 16,129 (excluding ROF Leeds).[10]

Re-orientation and re-organisation

With the creation of Royal Ordnance plc (RO), and later the sale to British Aerospace, a rationalisation of the number of factories within Royal Ordnance was inevitable, especially when RO was faced with the loss of preferred contractor status for the MoD, and open market competition from the other 25 ordnance companies in western Europe.[11]

One obvious anomaly in the new company structure was the

Plate 6.10 (ref G/4313c). One of the most innovative products designed and made at ROF Chorley in the 1970s, and still being made in the 1980s, was this signalling system called 'Dial a Star'. The signal 'stars' were contained in a cassette-type magazine which clipped to the top of the firing handle.

Plate 6.11 (ref 86). The Dial a Star signal system is seen here undergoing test firing. The system utilised coloured stars which could be 'dialled' in the magazine to fire a colour sequence of stars. The string lanyard, used to cock the trigger, could be looped around any projection, which might be required if the user was injured in some way.

role of the three agency factories. These were relics from the Second World War when Royal Ordnance work was undertaken by private companies on sites owned by the government. These factories were dedicated to RO work and charged on a pre-agreed basis. Such an arrangement did not make sense for the newly privatised Royal Ordnance which was itself a private company, albeit wholly owned by the government at this stage. Featherstone was used by ROSM, a joint venture company comprising Royal Ordnance and Sandrik Ltd, which later became a wholly-owned subsidiary of Royal Ordnance. Summerfield was integrated into the new company by its purchase from Imperial Metal Industries, whilst at Powfoot there continued to be joint arrangements between RO, now the main shareholder, and ICI.[12]

The new company had to face its over-dependence on one customer, the MoD. A document from 1985 prepared by the

accountants James Capel & Co for Royal Ordnance plc noted that '. . . the objective of Royal Ordnance's management is to significantly diminish its dependence on MoD business. There are several problems to overcome before this can be achieved, most importantly the somewhat limited export appeal of product lines which have been designed with usually only one customer in mind – the MoD. Tending to be over-specified and expensive, many Royal Ordnance defence systems are not particularly suited to the needs of overseas customers ... Both those factors have or are changing for the better with a commitment within Royal Ordnance to exploit new technology and design commercially viable products for internal markets.'[13]

In 1987, after the sale of the company to British Aerospace, an agreement known as EPREP was reached with the Ministry of Defence whereby greater competition would be gradually introduced into its contracts with Royal Ordnance. RO would supply products to the MoD at a fixed price for a period of five years from 1988 to 1993 (worth approximately £400 million per annum). Over this period the price per unit would be reduced,

Plate 6.12 (ref 3.1916). Within the Factory Quality Control Department, was 'calibration', which comprised some 25 or so personnel. The calibration section was responsible for the accuracy of all electrical and mechanical gauging equipment used during the production of all ammunition made on the factory.

Plate 6.13 (ref CF).
The employees of
ROF Chorley have
always played a large
part in the raising of
money for various
charities. This often
necessitated using
some rather unusual
garments! In the event
shown above, Group 3
personnel are playing
a football match with
a difference! The men
had to play in dresses
and wellies, and the
girls in normal
football kit!

Plate 6.14 (ref VIS). It
was often part of the
group training officer's
duties to meet visiting
VIPs. Visits such as
this were
commonplace, when
high ranking services
officers would tour the
factory, looking at
manufacturing
processes and talking
with employees.

forcing Royal Ordnance to become more efficient.[14] In an attempt
to broaden its client base RO took over the small arms manufacturer Sterling Armament Company Ltd, based at
Dagenham.[15]

In order to increase the viability of the new company fixed
costs had to be reduced, and one area where cuts could be made
was in the workforce. Initially, reductions in the workforce were
small, the total workforce dropping to 18,989 by the end of 1985.[16]

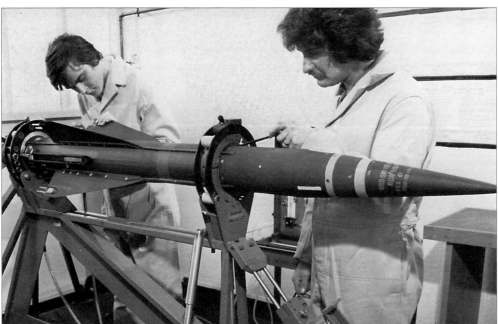

Plate 6.15 (ref 10/2076c). During 1980, the former Group 4 South, referred to as the 'Gunpowder Factory', saw most of its buildings demolished, the magazines being refurbished. On the group, new buildings were erected, for the production of the LAW 80 anti-tank missile system. During building, shown here in 1992, the site was reminiscent of the 1930s' building of the factory.

The demands imposed on Royal Ordnance by its new commercial contracts with the MoD, and later by market competition, led to a review of the number of sites run by Royal Ordnance. In 1988 RO Enfield became the first Royal Ordnance site to close since ROF Pembrey in 1962.[17] This was followed in 1989 by RO Patricroft.[18] The historic research and development site at Waltham Abbey was closed in 1989, its work being divided between the Ammunition Division (including RO Chorley) and the Rocket Motor Division.[19]

The dismantling of the Warsaw Pact in 1989/90 and the unification of Germany led to a lessening of tension between the East and West, with a direct impact on defence expenditure; there were reductions throughout the 1990s by both Britain and other western European countries.[20] An illustration of this lessening of tension was the visit by a group of Russian businessmen to RO Chorley in 1993, for the first time since 1943.[21] Nevertheless, the impact on Royal Ordnance plc was severe, with a sharp drop in orders ultimately leading to factory closures.

RO Chorley under British Aerospace: the Ammunition Division

Plate 6.16 (ref PM). The 1980s saw the production of guided weapon systems, 'all up round'. This had begun with 'Swingfire'. The same shop on Group 3 x-ray saw another missile introduced by the mid 1980s. This was Rapier. The missile bodies were received at Chorley, where they were fitted with their live warheads, after which they were refitted in their launch box.

Initially, RO Chorley benefited from these changes. Although large areas of the site had lain mothballed since the late 1950s, it became the headquarters of the Ammunition Division, and saw the refurbishment of the main administrative buildings during 1988–89.[22] With the closing of Waltham Abbey it became the chief research and development centre for the new company, and the base for the newly created Corporate Market Intelligence Unit in 1989.[23] The closing of RO Patricroft also lead to the transfer of a significant amount of work on the LAW 80 (Light Anti-tank Weapons) programme, and on the production of GW (guided weapon) components.

By 1991 RO Chorley employed around 1,600 people, with 100 in the Royal Ordnance plc headquarters, 400 in the Ammunition Division Headquarters and 1,100 in the remaining production facilities.[24] The production facilities were heavily reliant on two large contracts carried over from the pre-privatisation era. These were the MLRS (Multi-Launch Rocket System) project and the

161

Plate 6.17 (ref 1.3168c). Another part of the factory which saw refurbishment during the early 1980s was Group 1 West. Here again some old buildings were demolished and others refurbished. The principal new building here would be for the production of Boxer Caps for 5.56mm ammunition.

Plate 6.19 (ref 9.7434c). The factory has always helped with the raising of funds for local charities etc. One of the annual events is a sponsored raft race, which takes place on the River Ribble. Here we see one of the ROF teams testing their raft on the reservoir at ROF Chorley in 1986.

LAW 80.[25] Since these were products specifically designed for the MoD their long term viability and saleability abroad were in doubt.

The Ammunition Division also continued to manufacture a variety of ammunition from 5.56mm calibre up to 155mm for use on land, at sea and in the air. Products included conventional tank artillery and mortars, advanced missile warheads, grenades and sophisticated pyrotechnic devices.

Plate 6.20 (ref FT). The late 1980s saw the need for the demolition of the Centre for Management Studies, seen here in the background. In front of the building was an emergency water tank, which also had to go, even though it was full of fish! These were netted and removed prior to draining the tank. Seen here are the Factory Fire Brigade and design & development staff, during the netting.

Plate 621 (ref 9/7354c). When new production facilities, such as Boxer Cap and LAW 80 opened, they drew a lot of attention. In this view the LAW 80 system is being demonstrated by Mr T. Travis (right), watched by, from left, Director T. Jebb, Sir A. Hall, Executive Director, and Mr H. Butterworth, Managing Director. Photographed February 1986.

Plate 6.22 (ref 9/7599c). The decision to set up Royal Ordnance Ammunition Division Headquarters at the Chorley site meant an influx of new staff. Temporary offices had to be built because refirbishment of 10C18 and 10C30 was still in progress.

Plate 6.23 (ref 9/8348c). During the late 1980s, following privatisation etc, the workforce needed some reassurance, re: their future and their jobs. To meet this need, Managing Director Mr P. Kenyon toured RO sites to address employees about their concerns. At RO Chorley, the meeting with employees was held in South Side canteen, as shown in the plate above.

Plate 6.24 (ref 15). March of 1989 saw the 50th anniversary of the opening of ROF Chorley by King George the Sixth in 1939. To celebrate the 'Golden Jubilee', Mr Simon Towneley, Lord Lieutenant of Lancashire, officially opened the newly refurbished building 3A8, by Leyland Gate, as the new site admin building. Mr Towneley is seen here unveiling a plaque to mark the occasion.

Aside from the refurbishment of some of the buildings on the RO Chorley site, the main impact of the purchase of Royal Ordnance by British Aerospace was the partitioning of the RO Chorley site in June 1989. The area south of the railway line became the administrative headquarters for the Ammunition Division, whilst production, research and development, and the Fire Brigade section, were concentrated north of the railway line, with main access from the Leyland gate.[26] The two were physically separated by a barrier, and were to function independently of each other. This was a significant moment for RO Chorley. The original factory had been designed as a single coherent unit, so the physical splitting of the site was a clear indication of RO Chorley's changing status.

Other new facilities and projects undertaken immediately after British Aerospace's purchase of Royal Ordnance included the construction of the Fast Event Facility and research into bomb blast containment. Construction of the Fast Event Facility (FEF) began in 1990 – and opened in November 1991 at a cost of £1 million. It was intended to be used for exploding warheads and other explosive devices in controlled conditions within a reinforced chamber which would have sensors and cameras to record the events.[27] Between 1991 and 1994 research was undertaken at

RO Chorley into the creation of a bomb-proof aircraft baggage hold.[28] This work was extended to produce a bomb-proof litter bin after the Warrington terrorist bomb incident in 1993.[29]

RO Chorley was not immune to the long-term decline in defence related jobs, both within Royal Ordnance and nationally. A report in 1991 on the future of the factory recognised that the greater competition introduced by the government into the defence market since 1985, and the need to maintain quality and reliability, would inevitably mean reductions in staffing at RO Chorley.[30] Between 1992 and 1995 three events were to dramatically alter RO Chorley's position as a production facility. Firstly, it was decided in December 1992 to relocate the large shell filling capacity to RO Glascoed, a shift which had been completed by June 1995. Although this only affected around 30 jobs it involved the movement of both existing machinery and some of the filling workers, and was a symbolic break with the past, since shell filling had been transferred to ROF Chorley from ROF Glascoed in 1940.[31] Secondly, in June 1993 the LAW 80 programme came to

Plate 6.25 (ref 9/8983c). With the demolition of the Centre for Management Studies on the factory, the need for 'tutorial' accommodation was at a premium in the early 1990s. During this time, courses and lectures etc were held at venues outside the factory. This picture was taken at Astley Hall, a mile or so from ROF Chorley. A safety course was being held at the Inn on the Park nearby.

Plate 6.29 (ref IAF 006). The late 1980s saw the demolition of the former 'Group S' building 508. It was replaced by a new building, for the production of MLRS grenades or bomblets. Production of these continued in this building until production came to an end in 1995 (the same year as the last shells were filled on the factory). The MLRS building is shown here following its closure.

an end, with the completion of all final orders.[32] Thirdly, a body blow to production was dealt by the ending of the MLRS production programme in June 1995, with the loss of around 270 jobs, and the ceasing of production of the LAWs around the same time.[33] The ending of the LAW 80 programme was a result, in part, of its failure to find an overseas market, perhaps as a consequence of its exclusive design by the MoD for the MoD before 1985. Despite the securing of further orders for the site in 1996 and 1997 more redundancies were announced at RO Chorley in July 1998 which reduced the workforce to 406.[34]

In 1979 there had been 3,900 people employed at ROF Chorley, a figure which had dropped to 2,100 in 1989[35] and declined further to 1,600 in 1991, 900 in 1993, and 495 in 1997.[36] This steady decline, with most jobs being lost in the manufacturing and munitions filling sections of the factory,[37] was part of a trend across the whole of the defence sector. Jobs were falling due to reductions in defence expenditure, increased military specialisation by the government (as in the Trident programme) and technological advances.

The end of the factory culture

After 1984 the social life of the factory continued as before until the group system was dismantled as a consequence of the large-scale redundancies of the mid-1990s. The sports club remained a popular focus of activity, and the building was completely rebuilt in brick in 1990.[38] Football, cricket, hockey, bowling, table tennis, snooker and fishing competitions continued to be held there, prior to its sale after 1993.[39] Inter-group rivalry also continued until the group system ended, with the annual competition for the best 'good housekeeping' group; a competition whose origins lay in the Second World War, and which was designed to promote safe working practices and a safe environment.

The links between the factory and the local community had always been strong. A branch of the Boy Scouts had been founded at ROF Chorley in 1948, the First Euxton (ROF) Scout Troop,

Plate 6.31 (ref IAF 4P14). The LAW 80 anti-tank weapon system was produced at RO Chorley until 1993, when the contract came to an end. The production facility, with its computerised filling system, had become redundant, yet it was hoped that the refurbishment of the weapon system may provide work for the plant in the future. This view shows the main production building with its tall lightning conductors in 1996.

Plate 6.32 (ref 29/13A) The late 1990s have seen a large part of RO Chorley site closed, and ammunition filling removed to RO Glascoed, yet production still continues on the former Group 1. Some of the closed building have now been demolished, their 1930s concrete and reinforcing make up proving a worthy 'adversary' to modern demolition machinery.

and it celebrated its fortieth birthday in April 1988. The troop was formed with affiliations to the factory because parents of many of the boys worked there and lived in the factory houses close by. Their first 'hut' was close to South Side canteen, although this was later moved to a nissen hut located close to the factory South West Stores buildings.[40]

The late 1980s saw an annual intake of 15 year old pupils from St Michael's school in Chorley, who came on work experience for a period of a week. During their time in the administrative offices they were able to experience several of the departmental tasks. This event continued for several years.

RO Chorley's Golden Jubilee, in 1989, was marked by a number of events. A visit was arranged for four former Woolwich Arsenal men who had transferred to ROF Chorley 50 years previously. James Brown, Ted Callow, Charles Mitchell and Harry Percival, spoke to senior staff about their experiences at the 'infant' factory of the late 1930s.[41] To commemorate the King's opening of the factory on 31 March 1939 the new administration block was opened exactly fifty years later in a special ceremony whose guests

169

included local MPs, mayors and senior factory staff. The guest of honour was Mr Simon Towneley, Lord Lieutenant of Lancashire, who opened the building. As in 1939 this was followed by a tour of the site, lunch in the senior staff dining room and the Lord Lieutenant was the last to sign the old visitors book, begun by the King in 1939.[42] Another part of the jubilee celebrations saw the Granada TV company filming a documentary at the factory entitled 'Women in Munition Works'.[43]

Regeneration plans

By the end of 1994 RO Chorley had been reduced to two operational areas (Group 1 where Boxer Cap was located and Group 4N, the site of Chorley's research and development section) with a total workforce of around 600 on a site covering 236 acres. Most of the site (651 acres) had long been mothballed, but under the new commercial climate the decision was taken to make this area redundant, although the factory itself remained a divisional headquarters and the company headquarters.[44]

As early as 1991 the need for a strategy for the long term redevelopment of the site was identified, and in December 1994 this was published. This strategy envisaged the creation of an environmentally sustainable 'Urban Village' on 'brownfield' land. The key concepts for this proposal were 'mixed' development (commercial, industrial and residential), high environmental standards, reduced reliance on the private car by a serious commitment to public transport and the provision of an effective footpath and cycle network, and a balanced long term view on planning and investment decisions'.[45] In a number of ways this strategy would involve a return to the past through the recreation of 275 acres of greenspace, and the re-opening of the ROF Halt.

The first stage of this redevelopment proposal is the reclamation of the derelict and contaminated land on the site. RO Chorley represents one of the largest redundant industrial sites in the North West. An inherent risk of the munitions filling process is the contamination affecting both the buildings and occasionally the landscape. Since over half the buildings on the site have been used for processes which may have resulted in explosives contamination of the building fabric, remedial measures will need to be taken by burning them prior to demolition. The specialist nature of most of the buildings on the site make them unsuitable for alternative use, so many will, in due course, be demolished. This process has already begun on Groups 3W and 8, which are part of the redundant site. The factory housing estate has also been demolished and new houses built during 1998.

Other steps have also been taken to eleviate some of the local unemployment created by the run-down of RO Chorley in the mid-1990s. In 1994 the Chorley Business and Technology Centre was opened. This project is a joint venture between Royal Ordnance, Chorley Borough Council and the Chorley Local Enterprise Agency. It has accommodation for up to 20 small businesses, including nine workshops, all of which had been leased by 1997. Consequently a second stage of the centre has been built. In 1998 production of automotive safety systems began on the former Group 1 site and is a response to the increased safety awareness in the motor industry. The work at Chorley involves the production of actuators powered by small explosive devices for pre-tensioning of seat belts, and the severing of electrical power and fuel supplies following a crash.

The future

1999 marks the 60th anniversary of the filling factory at Chorley, and whilst most of the site is now decommissioned, approximately 238 acres of the original 928 acre site purchased in January 1937 is retained as a production facility (the former Groups 1 and 4 North), with enough capacity for an increase to the existing production output of electric caps and detonators, together with the manufacture of explosive compositions needed for this work. The Proof Yard, Fast Event Facility and Burning Ground are still within the production area, whilst Chorley remains the head office for Royal Ordnance plc.

The development of the ROFs, and later Royal Ordnance plc, ran parallel to that of the British defence industry. Consequently, ROF (later Royal Ordnance) Chorley always was and still is a direct reflection of government policy. Its construction was the result of a deliberate policy to create and maintain a state owned

ROF Chorley and the 'Bouncing Bombs' 1943

A great many stories surround the bombs used by RAF 617 Squadron to breach the German dams in the Ruhr during May 1943. The film of the raid, *The Dam Busters*, still arouses much interest in the development and deployment of the 'bouncing bombs', which were shown as being perfectly round! This was done for security reasons, still in force when the film was made in 1955.

The bombs were in fact cylindrical, some five feet long by four feet in diameter. These were filled with over three tons of explosive, and fitted with three hydrostatic detonating devices, similar to depth charges, and with 'self-destruct' delays.

Ex-employees of Chorley talk of filling the bombs on Group 6, and of their despatch from the factory. Hard evidence, however, is difficult to find, although research via the Public Records Office, the RAF Museum, the Imperial War Museum, and RAF 617 Squadron, does point to ROF Chorley. John Sweetman, in his book *Operation Chastise: The Dam Raid; Fact or Fiction?*, writes that 'the filling of the cylinder with HE had begun at Chorley' in April 1943. RO Glascoed also claimed that they were the fillers, and the lack of real proof as to who exactly did fill them is testament to the strict security which surrounded the bouncing bomb.

No English drawing of the bomb appears to have survived to the present day, but amazingly a German drawing does exist! Shown below, the drawing gives dimensions and filling details which were obtained after one of the planes carrying the bombs crashed during the March 1943 raid. The self-destruct mechanism failed in one of the bombs, allowing the Germans to recover it, complete with its launch system.

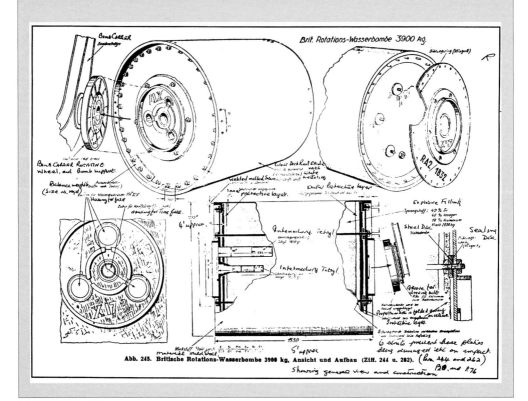

Abb. 245. Britische Rotations-Wasserbombe 3900 kg, Ansicht und Aufbau (Ziff. 244 u. 262).

172

The bombs used on the dam raid on 16 May 1943 were of the cylindrical type. Their development name was 'Upkeep', suffixed by 'Mine'. Another type of bouncing bomb was designed for use against shipping, but, although developed, it was never used 'in anger'. This bomb was called 'Highball', and was flat sided with a curved edge, similar to an aircraft tyre.

During 1993, 50 years on from the dam busting raid, the company magazine *Profile* featured an article on the bombs. Shortly after this, in 1996, off the Kent Coast, some of the bombs used in practice runs during 1943 were recovered, including a full sized Upkeep. The total weight of each bomb was 9,250lbs, 6,600lbs of this being RDX explosive.

The above illustration shows one of the bouncing bombs secured to the underside of Guy Gibson's Lancaster Bomber, prior to the raid on the Ruhr dams. The planes were fitted with a system which put backspin on the bombs just prior to release. The correct speed of the backspin in rpms was crucial to the successful deployment of the bombs.

and run defence industry. Its size and the scale of working during the war were a reflection of Britain's war effort. The maintenance of the site long after the war, at a much reduced level, with over half the factory mothballed, reflected successive governments' belief in a state owned defence industry. This changed with the arrival of a radical Conservative government in 1979 which saw open competition as the best way of reducing costs and maintaining quality and reliability.

More than any other event, even the ending of the Cold War and the subsequent decline in defence expenditure amongst NATO alliance countries, it was privatisation in 1985 that marked the most decisive shift in government defence strategy in over 50 years. This led directly to a reduction in the workforce at RO Chorley and many other Royal Ordnance factories due to increasing mechanisation and the need to compete effectively in an open market. The continuance of a vigorous defence industry and the survival of RO Chorley into the late 1990s is, in no small measure, due to British Aerospace and Royal Ordnance's commitment to quality and reliability of production, and to the continued dedication of the staff employed at the factory. ROF Chorley was unique; the biggest munitions filling factory in the world built by the government in three years to serve the needs of the nation in the face of an imminent global war. It is highly unlikely that such a site will ever be needed again, and so consequently ROF Chorley will always remain second to none.

Notes

Notes to Chapter 1

1. Farrer & Brownbill 1908; Mills 1976, 82. The origin of the name Euxton appears to stem from a Saxon name, Aefic combined with the Anglo-Saxon word *tun*, meaning a farm or settlement; thus meaning 'Aefic's farm/settlement', although where precisely this was is unclear. Euxton is first mentioned in the documentary record in 1187, when it was called 'Eueceston'. The name underwent a number of changes over the centuries; in 1311 it was 'Huxton' and by 1598 it was 'Extoburgh'.

2. *Profile* (November 1988), 6–7.

Notes to Chapter 2

1. RO/ROF/A3 Mack Smith 1944, 4–15.
2. Hay 1949, 7–15; RO/ROF/A3 Mack Smith 1944, 1–12.
3. PRO/Cmd. 229 Report of the Committee of Enquiry into the Royal Ordnance Factories, March 1919.
4. RO/ROF/A3 Mack Smith 1944, 16–28.
5. Crozier 1997, 113–4.
6. Crozier 1997, 114.
7. Crozier 1997, 114.
8. RO/ROF/A3 Mack Smith 1944, 71–7.
9. RO/CHO/A1; Hay 1949.
10. RO/ROF/A3 Mack Smith 1944, 36.
11. RO/ROF/A3 Mack Smith 1944, 36–8.
12. Birtill 1976, 64; *Chorley Guardian* 23/5/1936; Mack Smith 1994, 42.
13. Angell 1998; Birtill 1968, 77; Taylor Hutchinson & Partners 1990.
14. Hogg 1963, 1347.
15. RO/ROF/A3 Mack Smith 1944, 40–2, 49. The average house price in Britain in 1939 was between £300 and £400, which emphasises that the £12 million spent on building Chorley was a vast sum for the time.
16. *Chorley Guardian* 20/11/1937; RO/ROF/A3 Mack Smith 1944, 44–5; Smith 1989, 23.
17. RO/CHO/A5.
18. RO/ROF/A3 Mack Smith 1944, 43.
19. RO/ROF/A3 Mack Smith 1944, 38–9.
20. RO/ROF/A3 Mack Smith 1944, 50.
21. RO/ROF/A3 Mack Smith 1944, 51.
22. RO/ROF/A3 Mack Smith 1944, 52.
23. RO/ROF/A3 Mack Smith 1944, 53.
24. RO/ROF/A3 Mack Smith 1944, 54.
25. RO/ROF/A3 Mack Smith 1944, 45.
26. RO/ROF/A3 Mack Smith 1944, 47.
27. Birtill 1976, 75.
28. RO/ROF/A3 Mack Smith 1944, 48.
29. RO/ROF/A3 Mack Smith 1944, 48.
30. Birtill 1976, 87.
31. RO/CHO/D1 File on ROF Chorley staffing requirements c 1939–40; Hay 1949, 59–60.
32. Hay 1949, 56–8.
33. RO/ROF/A3 Mack Smith 1944, 49.
34. Birtill 1976, 85; 1/4/1939 *Chorley Guardian*; Smith 1989, 23.
35. 23/7/1938 *Chorley Guardian*.
36. RO Chorley Archives, photographs.
37. RO Chorley Archives, June 1939 report.
38. RO Chorley Archives, June 1939 report.
39. Verbal evidence from former Woolwich Arsenal/Chorley employee.
40. *Chorley Guardian*, 30/10/1938.
41. *Profile* (December 1988), 7.
42. *Profile* (December 1988), 7.
43. RO Chorley Archives, June 1939 report.
44. RO Chorley Archives, June 1939 report.
45. RO Chorley Archives, June 1939 report.
46. It is not the purpose of this section to deal exhaustively with the working practices within Royal Ordnance Chorley, which are better studied by consulting the twentieth-century factory regulations. Many of the working practices are unrecoverable archaeologically; however, others have left physical traces, and others can be recovered by using oral evidence; RCHME 1994, 157–9.
47. Verbal evidence from a former Woolwich Arsenal/Chorley employee.
48. Woolwich Arsenal Records 119/230 (226).

Notes to Chapter 3

1. Hay 1949, 22–3.
2. Hayes 1949, 23.
3. *The History of the Second World War.*
4. *The History of the Second World War.*
5. Hayes 1949.
6. *The History of the Second World War;* MacBean & Hogben 1990, 92–4.
7. The records have not survived to say precisely when.
8. MacBean & Hogben 1990, 63–90.
9. It is not known if Chorley filled the largest of the High Capacity bombs, the 22,000lb Grand Slam, although it seems likely; MacBean & Hogben 1990, 118, 130–7; *The History of the Second World War.*
10. *Profile* (December 1988), 7; personal reminiscences of four war time employees, James Brown, Ted Callow, Charles Mitchell and Henry Percival. These men were amongst the first 62 process workers to be transferred from Woolwich Arsenal.
11. MacBean & Hogben 1990, 158–62.
12. MacBean & Hogben 1990, 115–20.
13. RO/CHO/A4 '*ROF Chorley 1943*', report and staff handbook.
14. RCHME 1994.
15. RO/CHO/A4 '*ROF Chorley 1943*', report and staff handbook.
16. RCHME 1994, 46.
17. Most of these buildings survived in one form or another until the 1990s. Many original plans and elevations from the period 1937 to 1944 are still held at Chorley. For instance general plans for the two types of magazines, the shifting houses, processing buildings, canteens, boiler houses, Buckshaw and Worden Halls, and Passive Air Defence Systems (RO/CHO/A3 – World war II photos of ROF

Chorley; ROF Chorley Archives, *ROF Chorley Building Plans and Elevations, 1937–1944*). It was the intention of the present survey to record examples of the main building types in detail but the existence of these earlier plans, a survey by the RCHME in 1994, and individual photographic records made for each building that was decommissioned in the 1990s made this redundant.
18. Verbal information, former Woolwich/Chorley employee.
19. Summerfield 1984, 22.
20. 96 honours and awards were presented to ROF personnel during the war years for either outstanding service or bravery. These were mostly OBEs though the George Cross was awarded five times and the George Medal twenty times to Royal Ordnance staff. One George Medal was awarded to an employee at ROF Chorley. It was given to a Mr E. Ashcroft, a process worker, due to an incident that occurred on 22 September 194; we do not know what act of heroism he performed.
21. *The Factories Act*, 1937 and 1939.
22. The first overalls used at ROF Chorley were secured using ribbon fasteners; the concession of using rubber buttons was not introduced until 1943; *Home Office Pamphlet No 8*, HMSO 1938.
23. Chorley Archives, *ROF Chorley Report for 1941.*
24. Chorley Archives, Radio Room notes dated 1942.
25. Chorley Archives, RO/ROF/D18, *Closing Factories 1957–1962.*
26. Hay 1949, 98.
27. RO/ROF/D27 C05.
28. Birtill 1973, 25.

Notes to Chapter 4

1. French 1990, 212–24.
2. PRO AVIA 22/960, minutes dated 24 January 1945. The comments were by Sir George W Turner, Second Secretary to the Minister of Supply, in the first weekly departmental meeting held with the Minister of Supply and Aircraft Production.
3. PRO AVIA 22 960.
4. Hartley 1980; Greenwood 1972; Willett 1991, 35.
5. PRO AVIA 9/75 & AVIA 15/2247.
6. RO/ROF/D12 Half Yearly Report on the Filling Factories, January 1946 to July 1946.
7. Chorley Archives, RO/ROF/D18, *Closing Factories 1957–1962;* RO/ROF/D13 *Report of the Director General of Ordnance Factories For The Year Ended 31st March 1955*, 39; RO/ROF/D14 *Report of the Director General of Ordnance Factories For The Year Ended 31st March 1956;* Hay 1949, 73; Weinbren & Putnam 1995,

41–2; *The Times*, 22/10/1947. There is some dispute in the sources as to the precise number of factories kept and the figures of 21 and 22 have occasionally been cited. This confusion probably arises from the decision to begin re-arming in 1950 which saw the re-activation of a number of factories so that by 1957 there were 23 ROFs in production.
8. Chorley Archives, RO/ROF/D18, *Closing Factories 1957–1962;* RO/ROF/D13 *Report of the Director General of Ordnance Factories For The Year Ended 31st March 1955*, 43; RO/ROF/D14 *Report of the Director General of Ordnance Factories For The Year Ended 31st March 1956.*
9. Weinbren & Putnam 1995, 42–3.
10. Hay 1949, 72–4.
11. French 1990, 218–9.

12. Chorley Archives, RO/ROF/D18, *Closing Factories 1957–1962*.
13. Putnam & Weibren 1992, 104.
14. ROF Chorley Archives, *ROF Chorley Annual Report for 1951–52*.
15. Explosives Act 1875 and 1923; Explosive Regulations various dates.
16. ROF Chorley Archives, *ROF Chorley Annual Report for 1951–52*.
17. Verbal information from former Ammunition Dump worker, Mr G Clayton.
18. ROF Chorley Archives, *ROF Chorley Annual Report for 1951–52*.
19. ROF Chorley Archives, *ROF Chorley Annual Report for 1951–52*.
20. Verbal information from former Ammunition Dump worker, Mr G Clayton.
21. ROF Chorley Archives, ROF Chorley Annual Report for 1951–52. The date this list was compiled is unspecified but presumably it was done in early 1952 since the report runs to the end of March 1952. The quantities for each of the types specified was not given. Ammunition stored in boxes at Dawson Dump in 1952; SAP Incendiary and HE, in various box types; Oerlikon HE and HEI in various box types; Hispano HE and HEI in small boxes; Shell HE and HEI calibre/boxes various.
22. *Profile* 50 (December 1984), 8.
23. ROF Chorley Archives, *ROF Chorley Annual Report for 1951–52*.
24. Information from former ROF Chorley employee Mr D Aspinall.
25. Hay 1949.
26. As can be seen in examples in the villages of the Chorley area such as Charnock Richard, Euxton and Haghton; Information from personal records, Jack Smith.
27. The houses were made at the Chorley factory, according to one of the local residents.
28. ROF Chorley Archives, photographic records.
29. ROF Chorley Archives, photographic records.
30. *Chorley Guardian*, 10/12/1948.
31. *Chorley Guardian* 10/12/1948; *The Daily Telegraph* 18/10/1948.
32. RO/ROF/D12 Half Yearly Report on the Filling Factories, January 1946 to July 1946; Hay 1949.
33. RO/ROF/D12 Half Yearly Report on the Filling Factories, January 1946 to July 1946.
34. Hay 1949.
35. RO/ROF/D12 Half Yearly Report on the Filling Factories, January 1946 to July 1946.
36. ROF Chorley Archives, *ROF Chorley Annual Report for 1951–52*.
37. ROF Chorley Archives, *ROF Chorley Annual Report for 1951–52*.
38. RO/ROF/D18, *Closing Factories 1957–1962*.
39. ROF Chorley Archives, ROF Chorley Annual Report for 1951–52.
40. ROF Chorley Archives, ROF Chorley Annual Report for 1951–52.
41. RO/CHO/Report of Director of Ordnance Factories, Filling, 1955.
42. RO/CHO/A5.
43. RO/ROF/D18, *Closing Factories 1957–1962*.
44. RO/CHO/A5; RO/ROF/D13 *Report of the Director General of Ordnance Factories For The Year Ended 31st March 1955*, 204.
45. RO/ROF/D18, *Closing Factories 1957–1962*; RO/ROF/D13 *Report of the Director General of Ordnance Factories For The Year Ended 31st March 1955*, 204.
46. RO/ROF/D13 *Report of the Director General of Ordnance Factories For The Year Ended 31st March 1955*.
47. Work was sub-contracted to Ashdowns Ltd in St Helens, a subsidiary of Pilkington Glass Ltd. Interview with Harry Nevell, ROF Chorley employee 1955–6.
48. RO/CHO/A5.
49. RO/ROF/D22 *Report of the Director Ordnance Factories (Filling) for the Year Ended 31st March 1961*, 5; RO/ROF/D23 Report of the Director Ordnance Factories (Ammunition) for the Year Ended 31st March 1963, 5; Chorley Archives, *Royal Ordnance Factory Chorley* (Annual Report for 1972, 1); *Profile* 26 (April 1981), 10.
50. Hay 1949, 63.
51. *Lancashire Daily Post* 15/7/1947.
52. *Lancashire Daily Post* 16/7/1947.
53. ROF Chorley Archives, *ROF Chorley Annual Report for 1951–52*; Inman 1957; Summerfield 1984, 51–4.
54. ROF Chorley Archives, *ROF Chorley Annual Report 1951–52*.
55. *Ministry of Supply Apprentice Handbook, 1957*.
56. *Chorley Rural District Guide for 1948*.
57. *Chorley Guardian* 26/11/1954; 10/12/1954; 4/12/1956.
58. *Lancashire Life* October 1959; *Chorley Guardian* 3/4/1959; 1/5/1959; 2/8/1963.
59. *Chorley Guardian* 19/12/1947.
60. *Chorley Guardian* 19/9/1947.
61. *ROF News*, 7/11/1947.
62. *British Productivity Review* 26 (1956), 'Ammunition production'.

Notes to Chapter 5

1. PRO/Cmnd. 124, *Defence: Outline of a Future Policy*, HMSO, 1957.
2. RO/ROF/D21 *Note for Permanent Under Secretary of State by CROF May 1960.*
3. *Profile* 1 (December 1975), 3; *Profile* 50 (December 1984), 6–7.
4. *Profile* 1 (December 1975), 1.
5. ROF Chorley Archives, *Report of the Royal Ordnance Factories Organisation for the Year 1977–8*, 1.
6. RO/ROF/D21. *Note for Permanent Under Secretary of State by CROF May 1960.*
7. RO/ROF/D21. *Note for Permanent Under Secretary of State by CROF May 1960.*
8. ROF Chorley Archives, *Report of the Royal Ordnance Factories Organisation for the Year 1977–8*, 5.
9. *Profile* 3 (June 1976), 12; *Profile* 12 (June 1978), 1; Weinbren & Putnam 1995, 74.
10. ROF Chorley Archives, *Report of the Royal Ordnance Factories Organisation For the Year 1978–79*, 4–5; ROF Chorley Archives, *Report of the Royal Ordnance Factories Organisation for the Year 1979–80*, 8–9; ROF Chorley Archives, *Report of the Royal Ordnance Factories Organisation for the Year 1980–81*, 8. *Profile* 32 (June 1982), 1.
11. French 1990, 222.
12. ROF Chorley Archives, *Report of the Royal Ordnance Factories Organisation for the Year 1981–82*, 14.
13. *Profile*, 30 (December 1981), 1, 6; *Profile*, 32 (June 1982), 1.
14. ROF Chorley Archives, *Report of the Royal Ordnance Factories Organisation for the Year 1981–82*, 9, 15; ROF Chorley Archives, *Report of the Royal Ordnance Factories Organisation for the Year 1982–83*, 4–5; ROF Chorley Archives, *Royal Ordnance Factories Annual Report 1983/84*, 6–7.
15. *Profile*, 38 (November 1983), 1; *Profile* 44 (May 1984), 1, 3.
16. *Profile*, 37 (September 1983, 5); *Profile* 53 (March 1985), 9.
17. Ministerial speech quoted in *Profile* 32 (June 1982), 1.
18. *Profile*, 37 (September 1983), 1, 4.
19. *Ordnance Factories and Military Services. A Bill.* 19 December 1983. HMSO. The new divisions came into force on the 1st March 1984 (*Profile* 42, 1); ROF Chorley Archives, *Royal Ordnance Factories Financial Report for the period 1 April 1984 to 1 January 1985*, 9.
20. *Profile*, 42 (March 1984), 1, 3.
21. Weinbren & Putnam 1995, 74.
22. ROF Chorley Archives, *Royal Ordnance Factories Annual Report 1983/84*, 6–7; *Royal Ordnance plc, a presentation by James Capel & Co*, 7–8.
23. *Chorley Guardian* 19/5/1983, 30/6/1983, 13/10/1983;

Profile, 37 (September 1983), 3; *Profile* 41 (February 1984), 3.
24. ROF Chorley Archives, *Royal Ordnance Factories Financial Report for the period 1 April 1984 to 1 January 1985*, 4–5; *Profile*, 49 (November 1984), 3; ROF Chorley Archives, *Royal Ordnance Factories Centre for Management Studies*. Undated guide.
25. ROF Chorley Archives, *CROFs Report for 1957*.
26. ROF Chorley Archives, *CROFs Report for 1957*.
27. RO/ROF/D18, *Closing Factories 1957–1962*; RO/ROF/D22 *Report of the Director Ordnance Factories (Filling) for the Year Ended 31st March 1961*.
28. RO/CHO/D3 File re 'Maximum Production Potential: Single Shift Working', 1960; RO/ROF/D18, *Closing Factories 1957–1962*; RO/ROF/D22 *Report of the Director Ordnance Factories (Filling) for the Year Ended 31st March 1961*.
29. RO/ROF/D21 *Note for Permanent Under Secretary of State by CROF May 1960*; RO/ROF/D22 *Report of the Director Ordnance Factories (Filling) for the Year Ended 31st March 1961*, Appendix G1.
30. RO/ROF/D20 Royal Ordnance Factories (Filling). Group Symposium on the Automatic Factory.
31. ROF Chorley Archives, *Royal Ordnance Factory Chorley*, Annual Report for 1972, 3.
32. RO/ROF/D18, *Closing Factories 1957–1962*.
33. ROF Chorley Archives, *Royal Ordnance Factory Chorley*, Annual Report for 1972, 1–2.
34. RO/ROF/D23, *Report of the Director Ordnance Factories (Ammunition) for the Year Ended 31st March 1963*, Appendix H.
35. RO/ROF/D18, *Closing Factories 1957–1962*.
36. ROF Chorley Archives, *Quality Control (QC) Proceedures*.
37. ROF Chorley Archives, *AQAP One*, 1988 and *AQAP One*, issue 3, 1984.
38. *Profile*, 39 (December 1983), 6–7.
39. ROF Chorley Archives, *Royal Ordnance Factories Organisation for the Year 1982–3*, 16.
40. *Profile*, 67 (September 1986), 1, 6–7; *Profile* (May 1988), 6.
41. ROF ROF Chorley Archives, *Report of the Royal Ordnance Factories Organisation for the Year 1977–8*, 10; *Profile* 18 (August 1979), 14.
42. *Profile* March 1985.
43. *Profile* 68 (October 1986).
44. *Profile* 3 (June 1976), 6–7; *Profile* 7 (June 1977), 1, 7.
45. *Profile* 12 (June 1978), 9.
46. *Profile* 8 (August 1977), 6–7.
47. *Profile* 33 (September 1982), 1, 11.
48. *Profile* 20 (December 1979), 5.

49. ROF ROF Chorley Archives, Miscellaneous documents; timetables.
50. RO/CHO/A6 ROF ROF Chorley, Manuscript copy of the 1964 Silver Jubilee booklet.

Notes to Chapter 6

1. *Profile* 51 (January 1985), 1; *Profile* (August 1987), 7; Weinbren & Putnam 1995, 74.
2. *Profile* (February 1989), 1–2; *Profile* (July 1989), 3.
3. *Chorley Defence Industry Study. Report prepared for Chorley Borough Council.* Economic Development Consultants, May 1991, 9–12.
4. *Chorley Defence Industry Study. Report prepared for Chorley Borough Council.* Economic Development Consultants, May 1991.
5. *Profile* 64 (May 1986), 3.
6. ROF Chorley Archives, *Royal Ordnance Factories Financial Report for the period 1 April 1984 to 1 January 1985; Profile* 68 (October 1986), 4–5.
7. *Profile* 65 (June 1986), 1; *Profile* 66 (July 1986), 1–2.
8. *Royal Ordnance Vickers Special Bulletin* (August 1986), 1; *Profile* 68 (October 1986), 1. Nottingham continued to make the gun for the Challenger 2 Tank, which was manufactured at Leeds.
9. 9/4/1987 *Chorley Guardian; Profile* (April 1987), 1–2.
10. *Profile* (August 1987), 6–7.
11. *Chorley Defence Industry Study. Report prepared for Chorley Borough Council.* Economic Development Consultants, May 1991, 12–4; *Profile* (October 1988), 8.
12. Interview with Ian Maxwell, retired RO Legal Director.
13. *Royal Ordnance plc, a presentation by James Capel & Co,* 9.
14. *Chorley Defence Industry Study. Report prepared for Chorley Borough Council.* Economic Development Consultants, May 1991, 12–4; *Profile* (October 1988), 19.
15. *Profile* (June 1988), 1; *Profile* (August 1988), 1.
16. *Profile* (August 1987), 7.
17. RO/ROF/D21, *Note for the Permanent under Secretary of State by CROF May 1960*; RO/ROF/D18, *Closing Factories 1957–1962; Profile* (October 1988), 1; Putnam & Weinbren 1992, 116–7.
18. Weinbren & Putnam 1995, 76–7.
19. *Profile* (May 1988), 3.
20. *Chorley Defence Industry Study. Report prepared for Chorley Borough Council.* Economic Development Consultants, May 1991, 9–10.
21. ROF Chorley Archives, *ROF Chorley Visitors Book, 1939 to 1989.*

51. RO/CHO/A9 ROF ROF Chorley Newsletter, 1977–78.
52. *Profile* No 23 (August 1980).
53. *Profile* No 33 (September 1982).

22. *Profile* (November 1988), 12.
23. 29/4/1988 *Chorley Guardian; Profile* (December 1987), 1, 6–7. Royal Ordnance Chorley Archives M2 C05; *Profile* (July 1989), 2.
24. *Chorley Defence Industry Study. Report prepared for Chorley Borough Council.* Economic Development Consultants, May 1991, 12–4; *Profile* (October 1988), 22.
25. *Profile* (April 1989), 5.
26. *Profile,* March 1990.
27. *Profile,* December 1991.
28. *Profile,* October 1991; March 1992; March 1994.
29. *Profile,* June 1993.
30. *Chorley Defence Industry Study. Report prepared for Chorley Borough Council.* Economic Development Consultants, May 1991, 12–4; *Profile* (October 1988), 22.
31. *Lancashire Evening Post* 3/12/1992; 4/12/1992.
32. *Profile* July 1993.
33. *Profile* July 1995.
34. *Chorley Citizen* 13/8/1998; *Lancashire Evening Post* 17/7/1997; 19/7/21997.
35. 30/5/1991, 6/11/1992, 26/2/1993, 1/3/1993 *Chorley Guardian.*
36. 30/5/1991, 21/1/1993 *Chorley Guardian.*
37. 10/12/1992, 21/1/1993, 11/3/1993, 26/1/1994, 16/2/1994, 29/6/1994 *Chorley Guardian.*
38. *Profile* October 1990.
39. *Profile* December 1986 and November 1987.
40. *Profile* April 1988.
41. *Profile* December 1988.
42. *Profile* April 1989.
43. *Profile* May 1989.
44. *Chorley Defence Industry Study. Report prepared for Chorley Borough Council.* Economic Development Consultants, May 1991, 12–4; *Profile* (October 1988), 22; 25/1/1994, 10/1/1996 *Chorley Guardian; Lancashire Evening Post* 17/7/1997; 19/1/1997; 22/7/1997; 30/7/1997.
45. *Chorley Defence Industry Study. Report prepared for Chorley Borough Council.* Economic Development Consultants, May 1991; *Royal Ordnance Chorley Regeneration Masterplan.* Cass Associates in association with Environmental Services Group, Royal Ordnance.

Sources

Unpublished Material

Chorley Local Studies Library, Central Library, Chorley

Chorley Citizen, 13/8/1998.

Chorley Guardian, 20/11/1937; 23/7/1938; 30/10/1938; 1/4/1939; 19/9/1947; 19/12/1947; 10/12/1948; 26/11/1954; 10/12/1956; 3/4/1959; 1/5/1959; 2/8/1963; 19/5/1983; 13/10/1983; 19/4/1987; 29/4/1988; 30/5/1991, 6/11/1992, 26/2/1993, 1/3/1993; 25/1/1994; 10/1/1996.

The Daily Telegraph, 18/10/1948

Lancashire Daily Post, 15/7/1947; 16/7/1947.

Lancashire Evening Post, 3/12/1992; 4/12/1992; 17/7/1997; 19/7/1997; 22/7/1997; 30/7/1997.

Lancashire Life, October 1959.

The Times, 22/10/1947.

Public Record Office (PRO)

PRO AVIA 9/75, Papers on War Potential, May-August 1945.

PRO AVIA 22/960, minutes dated 24 January 1945 of a meeting between Sir George W Turner, Second Secretary to the Minister of Supply, and the Minister of Supply and Aircraft Production.

PRO/Cmd. 124, *Defence: Outline of a Future Policy*, HMSO, 1957.

PRO Cmd. 229, *Report of the Committee of Enquiry into the Royal Ordnance Factories*, March 1919.

PRO 15/2247, Papers on War Potential, September-December 1945.

Royal Ordnance Chorley Archives (RO) – Catalogued Material

Profile, The Newspaper of the Royal Ordnance, 1974 to 1998,. RO/ROF/E1.

RO/CHO/A1, File re visit of King George VI and a December 1939 Report for ROF Chorley.

RO/CHO/A3, World War II photos of ROF Chorley.

RO/CHO/A4, *ROF Chorley 1943*, report and staff handbook.

RO/CHO/A5, *Royal Ordnance Factory Chorley*. Report for 1958.

RO/CHO/A6, ROF Chorley, Manuscript copy of the 1964 Silver Jubilee booklet.

RO/CHO/A9, *ROF Chorley Newsletter*, 1977–78.

RO/CHO/D1, File on ROF Chorley staffing requirements containing maps, plans of district and staff charts , n. d., but c 1939–40.

RO/CHO/D3, File re 'Maximum Production Potential: Single Shift Working', 1960.

RO/ROF/A3, Mack Smith D, 1944, *Histories of Individual Royal Ordnance Factories 1881–1944*. Copy of a typescript history now in the PRO (CAB/HIST/R/4/2/2, CAB 102/625).

RO/ROF/D12, *Half Yearly Report on the Filling Factories*, January 1946 to July 1946.

RO/ROF/D13, *Report of the Director General of Ordnance Factories For The Year Ended 31st March 1955*.

RO/ROF/D14, *Report of the Director General of Ordnance Factories For The Year Ended 31st March 1956*.

RO/ROF/D18, *Closing Factories 1957–1962*.

RO/ROF/D20, *Royal Ordnance Factories (Filling). Group Symposium on the Automatic Factory*.

RO/ROF/D21, *Note for Permanent Under Secretary of State by CROF May 1960*.

RO/ROF/D22, *Report of the Director Ordnance Factories (Filling) for the Year Ended 31st March, 1961*.

RO/ROF/D23, *Report of the Director Ordnance Factories (Ammunition) for the Year Ended 31st March 1963*.

RO/ROF/D27, File of product information on Ordnance material, n. d.

Royal Ordnance Chorley Archives (ROF Chorley Archives) – Uncatalogued Material

ROF Chorley, *AQAP One*, 1988.

ROF Chorley, *AQAP One*, issue 3, 1984.

ROF Chorley, *CROFs Report for 1957*.

ROF Chorley, *Quality Control (QC) Procedures*.

ROF Chorley, Radio Room notes dated 1942.

ROF Chorley, *Report of the Royal Ordnance Factories Organisation for the Year 1977–8*.

ROF Chorley, *Report of the Royal Ordnance Factories Organisation For the Year 1978–79*.

ROF Chorley, *Report of the Royal Ordnance Factories Organisation for the Year 1979–80.*

ROF Chorley, *Report of the Royal Ordnance Factories Organisation for the Year 1980–81.*

ROF Chorley, *Report of the Royal Ordnance Factories Organisation for the Year 1981–82.*

ROF Chorley, *Report of the Royal Ordnance Factories Organisation for the Year 1982–83.*

ROF Chorley, *Royal Ordnance Factories Annual Report 1983/84.*

ROF Chorley, *Royal Ordnance Factories Financial Report for the period 1 April 1984 to 1 January 1985.*

ROF Chorley, *Royal Ordnance Factory Chorley*, Status Report for June 1939.

ROF Chorley, *Royal Ordnance Factory Chorley*, Report for 1941.

ROF Chorley, *Royal Ordnance Factory Chorley*, Annual Report for 1951–52.

ROF Chorley, *Royal Ordnance Factory Chorley*, Annual Report for 1972.

ROF Chorley, *ROF Chorley Building Plans and Elevations, 1937–1944.*

ROF Chorley Archives, *ROF Chorley Visitors Book*, 1939 to 1989.

ROF Chorley, *Royal Ordnance Factories Centre for Management Studies.* Undated guide.

ROF Chorley, *Royal Ordnance Vickers Special Bulletin* (August 1986).

ROF Chorley, factory construction photographs, 1937–39.

ROF News 7/11/1947.

Woolwich Arsenal, Records 119/230 (226), letter dated 24th June 1939.

Published Material

Angell, J M, 1998, *Worden Old Hall, Euxton, Lancashire.* Historic Building Survey Report for Msc Building Heritage and Conservation, Department of Built Environment, University of Central Lancashire.

Birtill, G, 1968, *Follow Any Stream.* Guardian Press, Chorley.

Birtill, G, 1976, *The Changing Years – Chorley and district between two wars.* Guardian Press, Chorley.

Chorley Defence Industry Study. Report prepared for Chorley Borough Council. Economic Development Consultants, May 1991.

Chorley Rural District Guide for 1948. Chorley Rural District Council.

Explosives Act 1875, *Public General Statutes 1875, 38 Victoria, ch 17; An Act to amend the law with respect to the manufacturing, keeping, selling, carrying, and importing gunpowder, nitro-glycerine, and other explosive substances.*

Explosives Act 1923, *Public Acts General 1923, 13 George V, ch 17; An Act to amend the Explosive Act, 1875.*

The Factories Act, 1937 and 1939. HMSO.

Farrer W & Brownbill J, (eds), 1908, *The Victoria History of the County of Lancaster*, vol. 3. Constable & Co.

French D, 1990, *The British Way in Warfare 1688–2000.* London, Unwin Hyman.

Greenwood D, 1972, 'Political Constraints upon Defence Expenditure', *Royal United Services Institute Journal* 119, March 1972.

Hartley K, 1980, 'The Political Economy of UK Defence Expenditure', *Royal United Services Institute Journal* 125, March 1980.

Hay, I, 1949, *ROF: Story of the Royal Ordnance Factories, 1939–48.* HMSO 1949.

The History of the Second World War.

Hodkinson, K, 1994, *Euxton Burgh.* Chorley.

Hogg, Brigadier O F G, 1963, *The Royal Arsenal. Its Background, Origin and Subsequent History. Volume II.* Oxford University Press.

Home Office Pamphlet No 8, HMSO 1938.

Inman P, 1957, *Labour in the Munitions Industries.* London.

MacBean J A & Heogben A S, 1990, *Bombs Gone. The development and use of British air-dropped weapons from 1912 to the present day.* London, Patrick Stephens Limited.

Mills D, 1976, *The Place-Names of Lancashire.* London, Batsford.

Ministry of Supply Apprentice Handbook, 1957. HMSO

Ordnance Factories and Military Services. A Bill. 19 December 1983. HMSO.

Postan MM, 1952, *British War Production.* London.

Putnam T & Weinbren D, 1992, *A Short History of the Royal Small Arms Factory Enfield.* Centre for Applied Historical Studies, Middlesex University for Royal Ordnance Division, British Aerospace Defence plc.

RCHME, 1994, *The Royal Gunpowder Factory, Waltham Abbey, Essex. An RCHME Survey, 1993.* Royal Commission on the Historical Monuments of England.

Royal Ordnance plc, a presentation by James Capel & Co.

Royal Ordnance Chorley Regeneration Masterplan, 1994, Cass Associates in association with Environmental Services Group, Royal Ordnance.

Smith, J G, 1989, 'Chorley Royal Ordnance Factory', *Chorley Historic and Archaeological Society Bulletin* No 15 (November 1989), 23–4.

Summerfield P, 1984, *Women Workers in the Second World War.* London, Croom Helm.

Taylor Hutchinson & Partners, 1990, *Buckshaw Hall, Chorley. Survey and Report relating to its Restoration for Royal Ordnance plc.*

Weinbren D & Putnam T, with the assistance of Cant D

and Hagger V, 1995, *A Short History of Royal Ordnance Patricroft. Nasmyth's Bridgewater Foundry*. Centre for Applied Historical Studies, Middlesex University for Royal Ordnance Division, British Aerospace Defence plc.

Willet S, 1991, 'Defence Employment and the Local Labour Market of Greater London', in L Paukert & P Richards, eds, *Defence Expenditure, Industrial Conversion and Local Employment*. Geneva.

Acknowledgements

Firstly, our thanks to Royal Ordnance plc for its commitment and vision in funding the research for this volume, and to the many Royal Ordnance plc members of staff who helped and advised in its production, in particular Chris Delahunt, Ginny Willcox, Clive Higginson, Dave Bury, Howard Prosser, Ian Maxwell, Trevor Collyer and Dr Malcolm Green. Thanks are also due to all current and former employees, too many to mention individually, who gave of their time in interviews and in the uncovering of fresh material, much of which was too detailed to be included in this volume but which has added immeasurably to the archives. To the staff of Chorley Local Studies Library, the Public Record Office and The Royal Commission on the Historical Monuments of England a special thank you for their help and advice. Finally, thanks to John Walker, Director of UMAU, all the staff at UMAU and the University of Manchester for their help and support; and to the other members of staff involved in the book, in particular researcher David Lloyd and proof reader Catherine Mackey.

Dr Michael Nevell and John Roberts of University of Manchester Archaeological Unit, and Jack Smith

List of Subscribers

NB. Gaps in the numerical sequence indicate where subscribers requested that their name should not be included in the list.

1 Mr D. Corner, Chorley
4 Nora Sherriff, Chorley
5 Richard Hough, Croston (employee, 1977–1991)
6 Mrs T. Holding, Charnock Richard
7 Miss E. V. Hall, Euxton
8 Mr and Mrs G. R. Harris, Euxton
9 William Billington, Leyland (Electrician, 1975–1985)
10 Thomas J. Arkwright, Chorley
12 Gilbert Walker, Chorley (40 yrs service, 4 yrs as Staff Side Chairman)
13 Margaret Wrennall, Clayton-le-Woods
14 Mrs D. Hughes, Euxton
15 Sally Brewer, Chorley (employed 1941–1945)
16 Jim and Emily Holden, Leyland
17 J. Newton, Chorley
18 Mrs E. Yates, Chorley
19 Mr H. Rex. Leyland, Chorley (ROF employee, 1941–1986)
20 Barbara M. Fowles, Chorley
21 Brian V. Smith, Chorley
22 Maureen Thompson, Chorley
23 Mrs Jennifer Fisher, Euxton
25 Mr F. Clitheroe, Chorley
26 Mrs B. Belcher, Euxton

27 Mr K. G. Bannister, Leyland
28 M. Sleddon and K. Sleddon, Euxton
29 Mrs Dorothea Darbyshire, Chorley
30 Miss Dorothy Gaskell, Chorley
31 Mr B. L. Sidebottom, Heath Charnock and Shap
32 Ian and Angela Thomas, Leyland
34 Mrs M. Howarth, Chorley
35 Mr Louis Hodson, Whittle-le-Woods
36 Norman and Maureen Hall, Chorley
37 Peter and Brenda Brunt, Bamber Bridge (formally Brenda Price)
38 Mr and Mrs Peter D. Hunter, Chorley
39 Margaret Gray, Heapey
40 Phil Tyrer, Whittle Springs
41 Mr W. E. Martin, Heapey
42 Mr R. Smalley, Chorley
44 Derek Bullock, Manchester
45 Annie Woods, Standish
46 Mr Boyd Harris, Whittle-le-Woods
47 Mrs D. M. Sephton, Chorley
48 Barry Jones, Chorley
49 Mrs Sheila Coleman, (née Furness) Chorley
50 Mr Les Barton, Leyland

52 Mrs J. Higgin, Leyland
53 J. J. Boyle, Heath Charnock
54 Phyllis Broadbent, Chorley
55 Mrs V. Lowe, Chorley
56 Kenneth and Joyce Riley, Chorley
57 Arthur Ellison, Bispham
59 Michael Pickering, Leyland
60 David O'Loughlin, Chorley
61 Mrs Elizabeth Ashcroft, Charnock Richard
62 Mrs Ella Salisbury, Sutton Coldfield
63 Frank Harrington, Walton-le-Dale
64 Mr T. Locke, Boston-Spa
65 Mr Michael Clifford, St Annes
66 Mrs M. Monk, Coppull
67 Dr S. E. Clayton and Mrs K. E. Clayton, Leyland
68 Mrs D. Jolly, Euxton
70 David John Sharrock, MIOSH. MCIOB, Leyland
71 Mark Cornwell, Higher Wheelton
72 Dorothy Bolan (Mrs), Euxton
73 Paul Rigby, Whittle-le-Woods
74 Mr and Mrs J. I. Catterall, Bolton
75 Jane Livesey (Mrs), Chorley
76 Mrs Anne Rostron, Charnock Richard

77 Mrs Eveline Bradshaw, Chorley
78 Mr Brian Longton, Coppull
79 Mrs Joan Ellithorn, Euxton
80 Mr Richard Smith, Chorley
81 Mr T. Fishwick, Leyland
82 Margaret Ainsworth (Mrs), Chorley
83 David Crofts, Bolton
84 Mr Ian Ordish, Heapey
85 Mr H. R. Dodson, Bolton
86 Rita R. Murray, Euxton
87 Graham Norris (Mr), Bolton
88 Mr and Mrs W. McCartney, Penwortham
89 J. K. Enderby, Chorley
90 Mrs Linda Wilson, Leyland
91 Pete Hatton, Bolton
92 Mrs Ruby O. Hamer, Leyland
93 Mr Alan F. Ogilvie C. Eng, Leyland
94 P. Lewendon, Euxton
95 Mr John Gibbons, Farington
96 Mr T. Kennedy, Chorley (employee, 1974-present)
97 Eric Jones, Euxton
98 Anthony Gee, Longridge
99 Esther A. Starkey, Leyland
100 Mr Ian Barrow, Leyland
101 Mr George Neil Fishwick, Chorley
102 Mrs M. Turner, Chorley
103 T. Smith, Chorley
104 Mr H. Baron, Chorley
105 Glyn David Jones, Euxton
106 Mrs E. Davies, Preston
107 Mr Keith William Roberts, Sale
108 M/S Catherine Drake, Bamber Bridge
109 Alan E. Pill, Chorley (Group 1 'L. Lines')
110 Alan Duxbury, Euxton
111 Alison Gass, Charnock Richard
112 James Rutter, Kirkham
113 Edward Tuson, Preston
114 David W. Millington, Euxton
115 George Ralph Millington, Chorley
116 Steve and Sue McNulty, Preston
117 John Mahoney, Wigan (employee, 1979-present)
118 Brian Holland, Wigan
119 John Larkin, Kent
121 Carl and Alison Burns, Euxton
122 Mike Hooper, Leominster
123 E. E. Jones, Euxton
124 Judith C. Hargreaves, Chorley
125 Mrs J. Williams, Preston
126 Barbara Barrow, Euxton
127 Mrs Florence M. Gregory, Coppull (née Barker)
128 John and Christine Fairbrother, Chorley
129 Mrs Y. Lancaster, Euxton
130 David Privett, Leyland
131 John Ashley, Blackburn
132 Miss Kath Smith, Leyland
133 Frank and Eileen Worley, Wigan
134 G. W. Sweeney, Chorley
135 Frank Pimblett, Wigan
136 Mr E. Kavanagh, Coppull (retired 1986, ex safety dept.)
137 David E. Beckett, Kent
138 Mr J. M. Williams, Wigan
139 Mr Peter Howarth, Wigan
140 Fred Martindale, Wigan
141 Mr R. Shaw, Chorley
142 Mr K. Tromans, Heath Charnock
143 P. L. Lyndon, Newton Abbot
144 Dr Gordon Bulloch, Leyland
145 Dr and Mrs M. H. Milnes, Chorley
146 Eileen and Harris Alston, Chorley
147 Ian Baxter, Leyland
148 Mr Benjamin Eccles, Preston
149 R. A. Lavender, Leyland
150 Mr Michael Davitt, Oswaldtwistle
151 Mary E. Winstanley, Euxton
152 Cyril Schultz, Leyland
153 John Richard Armitage, Chorley (electrician 1971–present)
154 Jean Armitage, Chorley (1975–1983 Group 8, 1989–1992 casual)
155 Mrs J. A. High, Coppull
156 Eric W. J. Ashton, Wigan (Electrician, ROF Chorley)
157 Kevin Robert Jones, Burnley
158 Peter Hicks, Chorley (ex ROF Technical Illustrator)
159 Kath Martin, Euxton
160 Mr and Mrs D. Fishwick, Farington
161 P. D. Nightingale, Darwen
162 Mrs Amy Parkinson, Leyland
163 Mr John W. Smith BEM, Chorley
164 Mrs T. Glover, Bamber Bridge
165 Bob Duffy, Clayton-le-Woods
166 E. W. Heyes, Euxton
167 D. R. Marshall, Euxton
168 Dennis Mower, Euxton
169 Ian J. Bentham, Euxton
170 Mrs Margaret Greathead, Cabus (employed Group 1)
171 Simon and Tracey Foster, Darwen
172 Mr Alan Beard, Shevington
173 David Fanning, Wigan
174 Alexander Keenleyside, Stockport
175 Alan John Caunce, Wigan
176 Marion Ainscough, Euxton
177 Keith Hunt, Gwent
178 Barry 'Wild Baz' Holden, Manchester
179 Keith Bowra, Rufford

180 Barry Ashton, Penwortham
181 Mrs Joan Higginson, Leyland
182 Mr Andrew Tucker, Runcorn
183 John Leonard Ellis, Chorley
184 Lt Col A. R. F. MacKenzie MSc JP, Chorley
185 Clifford Harrison, Wigan
186 Michael Hughes, Coppull
187 Geoffrey Alan Brown, Euxton
188 Mr Terry Jebb, Leyland (Factory Director, 1984–1986)
189 Frank Lythgoe, Bolton
190 Mr Stuart Wright, Wigan
191 Pauline Anyon, Walton-le-Dale
192 George Ian Bagshaw, Euxton
193 Alfred Brown ,1980–1993 and Pam Brown, 1958–1991, Chorley
194 Mrs E. Catterall, Coppull
195 Mrs Mary Gray, Euxton
196 Eileen Wolstenholme, Chorley
197 Peter James Ryding, Preston
198 Norman Haworth (40 yrs service), Pauline and Dale Brown, Chorley
199 W. Trevor Oates, Euxton (Catering Manager, 1975–1989)
200 Mr Duncan Bamber, Leyland
201 Susan Round, Chorley
202 Barbara Elizabeth Iddon, Chorley
203 Nicola Dean, Clatford
204 Gerald Mills, Chorley
205 Mr Harold Haworth, Chorley
206 Robert R. Barton, Leyland
207 G. Barlow, Coppull
208 John Graham Walmsley, Chorley
209 D. T. Olive, Preston

210 B. T. Pennington, Euxton
211 Gillian Sedgwick (Mrs), Kent
212 David S. Campbell, Worcester
213 Steven Robert Pilkington, Wigan
214 John Cartledge, Wigan
215 Mrs Patricia Horsley, Chorley
216 Phil Djali, Euxton
217 Mrs I. Crossthwaite, Preston
218 Peter Dally, Preston (worked in N.P.E.T.C.)
219 Mr Philip Painter, Swinton (Industrial Engineer 4 South)
220 Elizabeth Atherton, Blackrod
221 Mr Donald W. Hocking, Chorley
222 Mr R. J. Law, Lemmington Spa
223 Richard T. Harwood, Chorley
224 Anthony Eccles, Leyland
225 Mr Neil Holt, Blackburn (current ROF employee)
226 Mr J. Hammerton, Blackpool (Po No, 0719 7/2912)
227 Simon Latham, Coppull
228 David Latham, Coppull
229 Mr Christopher Briggs, Leyland (employed at the Naval Proof Yard)
230 Mrs N. Walton, Preston
231 Mr S. Bullivant, Heath Charnock (retired 1985)
233 Mr James Marginson, Westhoughton
234 Mr Henry Kitchen, Leyland
235 Stanley Elliott, Adlington
236 Mrs Mavis Dawson, Chorley (ROF Chorley, 1966–1992)
237 James Anthony Mordlock, Leyland

238 Mrs Marion Taylor, Coppull
239 Peter Wilson, Bamber Bridge
240 Sheila Sturgess, Chorley
241 Shirley Collinson, Chorley
242 P. A. England, Adlington
243 John Leigh, Chorley
244 Robert Wilson, Leyland
245 Steven Eddleston, Blackburn
246 Mr C. Ingham, Leyland
247 Brian Harrison, Morecambe (Safety Officer, ROF Chorley)
248 Patricia Bell, Preston
249 Mrs Doreen McCue, Euxton
250 Derek Aspinall, Euxton
251 Mrs Mary West, Leyland
252 Mr J. Woodcock, Chorley (Building Works Dept.)
253 Kathy White, Chorley
254 Ruth Whiteside (Mrs), Leyland
255 P. Labbett (Mr), London
256 Mr J. R. Fettes C Eng MR Ae S, Preston (died 29 March 1999)
257 Mrs Ann Grayken, Charnock Richard
258 Viv Roberts, Rufford
259 Mildred Duff, Ulnes Walton
260 Barbara A. Hacking, Blackburn (Executive Secretary, 1988–1998)
261 Stephen Cooper, Chorley
262 Irene Wallis, Coppull
263 Miss A. Dixon, Adlington
264 Mr P. Cunliffe, Standish
265 Mr W. T. Worsley, Euxton
266 Peter Allan Jeune, Leigh
267 Mr E. L. T. Lewis, Walton-le-Dale
268 Mr Alan W. G. Fraser, Glasgow
269 Carole Ann Cowling, Chorley
270 John Belshaw, Wigan

271 Margaret Tomlinson, Preston
273 Mr K. N. Belford, Manchester
274 Gillian Hughes (Mrs), Newton-le-Willows
275 Dr J. Gilks, Kilmacolm
276 Jack Lyon, Wigan
277 George Bennett, Ashton in Makerfield
278 Brian Gore (1971–1999) and Barbara Kendall Gore (1978–1989), Horwich
279 Kathleen Tyrer, Heath Charnock
280 Mrs Dorothy May Speak, Bolton
282 Charles Louis Nightingale, Chorley
283 J. L. Moore, Wigan
284 Mr J. R. Eskdale, Preston
285 Mr G. Crewe, Honiton
286 David Anderson, Accrington
287 Thomas A. Moore, Chorley
288 Carole Marsden, Wigan
289 John Featherstone, Wigan
290 Mr Keith Cobham, Euxton
291 S. M. Roberts, Euxton
292 Mrs C. Hartley, Euxton
293 Mrs Betty White, Leyland
294 Mrs P. M. Lunan, Leyland
296 Bert Smith, Chorley
297 Mr Alan Fairclough, Chorley
298 Mr R. A. Farrimond, Wrightington
299 Chris Almond, Leyland
300 Mr Thomas Ince, Chorley
301 Tom Topping, Preston (Electrician, Aug. 1971–July 1995)
302 Roy Parkinson-Truman, Anderton
303 Peter Adrian Gent, Chorley
304 Peter Duerden, Lower Darwen
305 Alan Taylor, Littleborough
306 Anthony Joseph Halshaw, Coppull

307 Doris Maureen White, Chorley (worked at ROF, 1979–1992)
308 C. Peter Walker, Wigan
309 Richard O. Watson, Whittle-le-Woods
310 Robert T. T. Crawford, Kirkham
311 Harry C. H. Perrett, Bamber Bridge
312 Mrs B. Arnold, Chorley
313 Mr P. Wainwright, Penwortham
314 Mr F. E. Ingham, Penwortham
315 Mr Norman White, Higher Wheelton
316 Peter Smallwood, Wigan (worked on Group 1 for 38 years)
317 Steelwise Fabrications, Leyland
318 Miss Janet F. Astley, Brinscall
319 Miss Barbara Yates, Heath Charnock
320 Peter Eagle, Leyland
321 Dr James Hedworth, Fulwood
322 Mr K. Rawcliffe, Darwen
323 Mr C. A. Wildig, Adlington
324 Lorraine Foulkes, Heath Charnock
325 Mr A. J. Lyddon, Woking
326 Leonard Heathcote, Manchester
327 Mr Peter Lyon, Leyland
328 Michael Rawlinson, Leyland
329 Frank Cowell, Blackpool
330 Mrs Ann Harlow, Euxton
331 Roy Stankard, Leyland (Site Photographer, 1968–92)
332 David Riding, Chorley
333 Mrs Margaret Sinclair, Chorley
334 John Fairclough, Anderton
335 Andrew Mountain, Euxton

337 P. G. Massey, Preesall
338 Mr and Mrs Eric and Freda Smith (25 and 31 years service)
339 Mr Neil Pennington, Manchester
340 Mr Richard Culshaw, Standish
341 J. C. Hall, Warrington
342 Steve Harris, Nottingham
343 D. W. Lyon, Leyland
344 Mr David Hoyle, Withnell
345 Peter Drinkwater, Sedbury
346 Dr Edward Blore Hancock, Leyland (ROF Chorley, 1958–1989)
347 Mrs Janet Glenda Watkinson, Chorley
348 Mr M. Chester, Euxton
349 Eva Grimshaw, Chorley
350 Gordon Grimshaw, Euxton
351 Beryl Ronan, Aspull
352 John R. Ideson, Preston
353 Patrick and Monica Cussens, Euxton
354 Mrs Elaine Tyrer, Chorley
355 Paul Boughey and Sue Boughey, Brindle and Mrs Jean Greenwood, Euxton
356 Don Waring, Feniscowles
357 Mrs S. L. Hazeltine, Euxton
358 Stephen Fielding, Feniscowles
359 Graham Forrest, Blackburn (21 years service)
360 Mr Anthony J. Palmer, Chorley
361 Piers Walker, Little Hoole
362 Melvyn Boocock, Penwortham
363 Mr George Edward Brooks, Eccleston
364 Bob Dolby, Chester
365 John Thompson, Chorley
366 Mr B. L. Warren, Chorley
367 Geoff Pengelly, Chorley
368 Ken Ward, Haugesund, Norway
369 E. Lloyd, Leyland

370 Mr J. S. Halliwell, Penwortham
371 Mr W. Polding, Standish
372 Roger Richards (Dr), Bridgewater
373 Carolyn Onslow, Coppull
374 Mr Bernard Moore, Bicester
375 Mr R. Gillett, Euxton
376 Steven Gerard Thomas, Shevington
378 A. Humphreys, Horwich
380 Keith Wilkinson, Leigh
381 W. A. Johnson, Low Ullermire, Kirklinton
382 Mr Walter Edge, Wrightington
383 Mr F. Taylor, Adlington
384 Harold Taylor, Chorley
385 Gordon Christie, Southport
386 John Young, Leyland (Fire Officer, 1984–1995)
387 Charles McLardie, Chorley
389 Mrs Enid Armstrong, Euxton
390 James Drake, Ribbleton
391 Mr R. Bankhead, Euxton
392 John Edward Dixon, Euxton
393 Patricia Rylands, Clayton-le-Woods
394 Miss A. M. Marsh, Leyland
395 E. J. McKenna, Charnock Richard
396 Mr J. A. Finch, Leyland (ex Naval Proof Yard)
397 E. Knight, Brimscall
398 Mrs Patricia Anne McGinlay, Manchester
399 N. J. Royster, Chorley
400 Mr Andrew Jack, Bamber Bridge
401 Mr E. Bolton, Chorley
402 Mr Keith Gaskill, Blackburn
403 Mr G. Senha, Leyland
404 E. C. Leach, Leyland
405 Mrs S. Clarke, Charnock Richard
406 R. D. Smith, Euxton
407 R. M. Collyns, Swindon

408 Dennis Butler, Heskin
409 Clifford Alan Ball, Whalley
410 Mrs Carol Ann Curry, Feniscowles
411 Mrs I. Sherburne, Chorley
412 Mr D. W. Hargreaves, Chorley
414 Mr Harry Prescott, Wigan
415 Mr E. A. Baker, Kidderminster
416 Rodney Boon ISM, Hoghton (Fitter Process Research Dept.)
417 Mr Frank Ferris, Sedbergh (former employee, 1947–1977, Engineer)
418 Johnny Glover, Euxton
419 Trevor Sansom, Buxton
420 John G. Doleman, Nottingham
421 Peter C. Edwards, Studley
422 John E. Rowley, (former employee)
423 George and Anne Slater, Blackburn
424 Jimmy Henry, Chorley
425 Mr T. G. Jervis, Croesyceiliog
426 Mr Alfred Roscoe, Wigan
427 Mr David Green, Usk
428 Mrs Lillie Williams, Porthmadoc
429 Mrs I. Gale, Leyland
430 Mrs Wanda J. Dawson, London
431 David Booth, The Gate House, Catterall
432 Mrs C. R. Levis, Cleveleys
433 S. Chadwick, Adlington
434 John Feenan, Clayton-le-Woods (employed 1977–1982)
435 Mr Harold A. Scott, Clayton-le-Woods
436 Norman Richard Heydon and Christine Heydon, Eccleston
437 Mr James Pennington, Euxton

438 Ian F. Freeman, Leyland
439 June Hill, Victoria (Australia)
440 Paul Allen, Queensland (Australia)
441 Kathleen Short, Rochdale (employed 1969–1989)
442 Andrew Donalds (1985–1998); Caroline Donalds (1978–1998), Euxton
443 John Higton, Long Eaton
444 Dr David Izod, Royston
445 Mr John Clancy, Wigan
446 Mr E. G. Pill, Euxton
447 Mr J. H. Cheyne, Chorley
448 Jack Monk, Chorley
449 R. A. J. Miller, Bristol
450 Mrs Lynda White, Chorley
451 Anthony Kilfoyle, Swinton
452 Mr T. J. Hilton, Heath Charnock
453 Glynne John Davies, Gwent
454 Mr V. H. Norris, Chorley
455 Mr Edward John Callow, Chorley
456 David W. Clark, Whittle-le-Woods
457 John Rall, Wigan
458 Matthew Morris, Wrightington
459 Mr William John Farrimond, Atherton
460 A. Vesty, Tyldesley
461 Mr Horace Nevin, Wigan
462 Mr George Farnell, Chorley
463 Mrs Margaret Ann Howarth, Euxton
466 Shelia Wareing, Leyland
467 Andrew Williams, Leyland
468 Mr J. R. Spink, Blackpool (employed 1956–1986)
469 Mr D. A. Roscoe, Chorley
470 Mark Andrew Short, Leyland
471 Mrs Margaret Holding, Chorley
472 Kevin Breen, Clayton Brook

473 Mr and Mrs F. Blackledge, Chorley
474 Colin Nickeas, Wigan
475 Lilian Rich, Euxton
476 Stephen (Sam) Marsh, Wigan
477 Michael Gibbons, Queensland (Australia)
478 T. J. AND J. A. Bailey, Lcyland
479 Mr David G. Brewer, Euxton
481 Mr T. J. L. Travis, Blackburn
482 Mr Graham Thomas, Leyland
483 Mrs Lavinia Rose Corfield, Wigan
484 Mrs M. A. Motyka, Euxton
485 Lt Col. (R) M. W. Newcombe GM, Chepstow
486 Dennis Olson Raw, Hoghton
488 Ian Maxwell, Lancaster
489 Colin Gee, Manchester
490 Mrs J. Starling, Euxton
491 Mrs Mavis Davies, Coppull
492 Keith Lewthwaite, Bolton
493 Dr G. Sykes, Bolton
494 John Roper, Tarleton
495 Mr Peter John Durber, Whittle-le-Woods
496 Dr I. S. Fox, Euxton
497 Don Young, Buckingham
498 Martin Trengove, Euxton
499 Miss Renee McNair, Bamber Bridge
500 D. Whittaker, Heath Charnock
501 Philip Clarke, Somerset
502 Alan E. Gallo, Abergavenny
503 Mrs E. M. Cook, Clayton-le-Woods
504 Mavis Hawkins, Eccleston
505 Neil Gregory, Eccleston
506 Mr M. K. Parker, Gateshead
507 Mrs Jean Higgins, Whittle-le-Woods
509 Martin Hearne, Chorley
510 Eric F. Nickson, Manchester

511 Frank Grimshaw, Wigan
512 Allan F. Rhoden, Up Holland
513 Frederick E. Rhoden, Shevington
514 Andrew Martin Swindale, Marple
515 Margaret Southworth, Ashton-in-Makerfield
516 Dr Roy Kelly, Whalley
517 Mr R. Townsend, Euxton
518 Mr D. Wildman, Tunbridge Wells
519 Allan Foster, Surrey (from friends at ROF Chorley, March 1999)
520 Daphne Carlin, Chorley
521 Alexander Latham, Chorley
522 Mavis Moss, Chorley
523 Mr G. R. Cutts, Euxton
524 Mr L. T. Haynes, Leyland
525 Michael James Doody, Bury
527 John D. Allan, Erskine
528 Jimmy Nisbet, Preston
529 Graham P. Dyke, Manchester
530 Mrs D. Graham, Leyland
531 Stephen Henwood, Hothersall
532 Stephen Hill, Adlington
533 John D. Heyworth, Chorley
534 Andrew Hayes, Leyland
535 Mr Bernard Moon, Euxton
536 J. Heskin, Brinscall
537 Mr Michael McNulty, Leyland
538 William Holt, Bolton
539 Christine Cleworth, Heath Charnock
540 M. J. Pruett, Chorley
541 Mr G. R. Bradshaw, Up Holland
542 Peter Evans, Euxton
543 Miss Elizabeth Ann Bettany, Leyland
544 John Gordon Taft, Kidderminster
545 Robert Helyard, Beverley
546 Miss Shelia Hill, Chorley

549 Brian Andrews, Clayton-le-Woods
550 Mr A. Moulton, Walkden
551 L. J. Jackson, Leyland
552 Mrs Joan Duxbury, Chorley
553 D. A. Rae, Manchester
554 Mr W. Moss, Penwortham
555 Martin Speirs, Stourport-on-Severn
557 R. Applin, Basingstoke
558 Mohammed Sajid, Chorley
559 H. Birchall, Leyland (Analytical Chemist)
560 Philip Preston, Bramhall
561 John Quinn Huey, Renfrewshire
562 Mrs Dorothy Owen, Horwich
563 B. Harlow, Chorley
564 Dennis J. Flynn, Manchester
565 Mr Brian Curwen, Chorley
566 Edith and Roy Renshaw, Euxton
567 K. J. Garry and J. Lawson, Coppull
568 Stephen Partington, Croston
569 John Ascroft, Stoke-on-Trent
570 Darren Nelson, Leyland
571 Mr Christopher F. Foss, Bordon
572 Steven Thomas, Bolton
573 Mr Roy and Mrs Catherine M. Wareing, Leyland
574 Mrs Elaine Lesley Clitheroe, Leyland
575 Marjorie Balshaw, Preston
576 Peter Eaton, Warrington
577 Mr Keith A. Byron, Wigan
578 Ms J. Ambler, Eccleston
579 Mr David W. Finan, Chorley
580 Mr Richard Bishop, Chorley
581 Mr Bruno Vaisnys, Chorley
582 Jim Kershaw, Blackburn
583 Bernard Gethings, Rimington

585 Dennis Parkinson, Coppull (on his 65th birthday, 5.5.99)
586 Bryan Brindle, Leyland
587 Mr E. Bramley, Euxton
588 Mr David Hannam, Dartford
589 Mrs E. Flaherty, Euxton
591 Don Staig, Heskin (30 years at ROF Chorley)
592 Julie Nelson, Chorley
593 John Unsworth, Charnock Richard
594 Barry Unsworth, Charnock Richard
595 Frank Unsworth, Charnock Richard
596 Jim Standish, Tyldesley
597 D. and C. Woosey, Leyland
598 Mr and Mrs John and Enid Turner, Euxton (Group 8 and components 3B5)
599 Mr William (Bill) Yates, Whittle-le-Woods
600 Linda Haworth, Ulnes Walton
601 Brenda Ellen Pennington, Wigan
602 Mr C. P. Exley, Croston
603 Alma Hughson, Chorley
604 Raymond Boardman, Bamber Bridge
606 Mr I. Walsh, Leicester
607 Mrs G. J. McDermott, Brinscall (retired 8–10–82, P & GS. C. X Ray Dept)
608 Dorothy Yates, Chorley
609 Dr Andy Clayton, Blackburn
610 J. M. Weldon, Euxton
611 Mrs M. R. Fowler, Chorley
612 Irene Vernon, Euxton

613 Mr Arthur Trafford, Chorley
614 Mrs E. M. Adams, Chorley
615 Mr P. R. Randall, Chorley
616 Ian B. Wilkinson, Croston
617 Mr and Mrs J. F. Goode, Coppull
618 Mr Stephen Lewis, Chorley
620 John Blake, Sunderland
621 Vaughan Seddon, Adlington
622 Mr Bryan Hughes, Aylesbury, Bucks
623 Mr M. Jones, Leyland (Transport)
624 Mr John Beech, Stoke-on-Trent
626 Mrs Vera Cooper, Leyland
627 J. D. Harrison, Hexham
628 Mr L. Kennard, Little Hoole
629 Mrs A. L. Phillips, St Austell
631 John Anderson, Euxton
632 Mrs Yvette Campell B. LIB (Hons), Cardiff
633 Leslie Fow, Chorley
634 Sidney McLarnon, Croston
635 Michael G. Peters, Standish
636 Mr A. E. Whalley, Atherton
638 M. W. Beswick, Chorley
639 Mrs Margaret Riding, Euxton
640 G. L. Weir, Chorley
641 Mr Roy Jackson, Chorley
642 Mrs B. Salisbury, Leyland
643 Mr D. Parkinson, Euxton
644 J. Wilkes, Salisbury
645 Mr Andrew Carrett, Abergavenny
646 Bill Gratton, Standish
648 Florence Worth (injured on 11.02.1941, died 19.02.1941)
649 J. F. Runeckles, London
650 Mr Derek Wren, Chorley
651 Brian Jeffrey, Penwortham

652 Arthur Yeager, Tampa, Florida
653 Ian Swallow, Whittle-le-Woods
654 Ross Bingley, Brinscall
656 Andrew R. Lumley, Alston
657 Stanley Ralph Pilkington, Hindley
658 Mr J. E. Mellors, Chorley
659 R. Rogerson, Coppull
660 Carol Swann, Whittle-le-Woods
661 M. J. Hulme, Chorley
662 Neil Barter, New Longton (employed 1975–1993)
663 J. M. Mackenzie, Euxton
664 Bryn Dawes, Letchworth
665 Murray Fullerton, Congleton
666 Brian Halliwell, Whittingham
667 Mr and Mrs F. A. Childs, Bamber Bridge
668 Mrs Margaret Hall, Leyland
669 Ellis Kay, Penwortham (Chief Group Officer, retired 1982 after 43 yrs)
670 Eva Bradshaw (Mrs), Leyland
671 Graham Trewhella, Southport
672 Clive Armitage, Chorley (engineering foreman, 1975–1991)
673 Cllr Jean E. Cronshaw, Chorley
674 Patrick Francis Maher, Poulton le Fylde (45 years service)
675 Mr Peter Charles Golder, Clayton-le-Woods (Senior Personnel Officer)
676 Richard Bailey, Preston